Solve It!

CROSS-WORD

To Lam
Hoping you enjoy
the book!
Miss you!

hinkler

hinkler

Published by Hinkler Books Pty Ltd
45–55 Fairchild Street
Heatherton Victoria 3202 Australia
www.hinkler.com.au

Puzzles © Puzzlexperts Publications 2012, 2014
Design © Hinkler Books Pty Ltd 2012, 2014

Images © Shutterstock.com: Lead pencils on white background © tolred

Cover design: Hinkler Design Studio
Typesetting: MPS Limited

ISBN: 978 1 7436 3518 6

Printed and bound in India

PUZZLES

CROSSWORD

PUZZLE 1

ACROSS

1. Fighting with lances
5. Retail outlet
7. Festive occasion
8. Dreamt
9. Commander
12. Reaffirm
15. Fell over
19. Felt the loss of
21. Native American weapon
22. Snatch
23. Hawaiian dance
24. Organism living off host

DOWN

1. Keep balls in air
2. Hot water burn
3. Chillier
4. Sideways look
5. Ghost
6. Sell on street
10. Molecule particle
11. Sinister
12. Purge
13. Hindu garment
14. Cultural pursuits
15. Spasm
16. Curved fruit
17. Pitch tent
18. Able to be eaten
19. Fabricator
20. Moans wearily

CROSSWORD

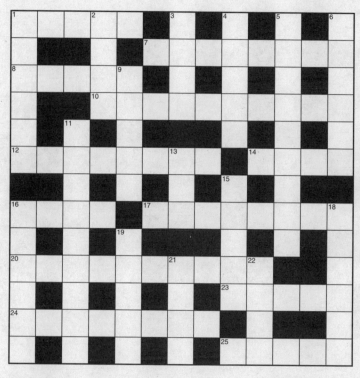

PUZZLE 2

ACROSS

1. Increases magnification, ... in
7. Wild prank
8. Appeal earnestly
10. Mythical Irish imp
12. Revive (interest)
14. Lose (fur)
16. Religious sisters
17. Diverges
20. Made assurances
23. Classified
24. Graceful style
25. Glided on snow

DOWN

1. Metal-toothed fastener
2. Breakfast or dinner
3. Operator
4. Ornate
5. Skydive
6. Rested (on)
9. Deferment
11. Storm cloud moisture
13. Ram's mate
15. Nile or Amazon
16. Lump of gold
18. Sown (with grain)
19. Covered-in canoe
21. Discretion
22. Badly-lit

CROSSWORD

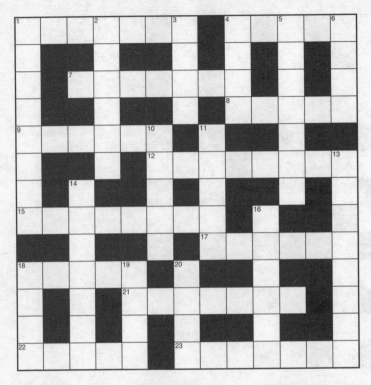

ACROSS

1. Grooming (hair)
4. Fashionable fad
7. Ocean-liner waiter
8. Greatly please
9. Grow (business)
12. Show up again
15. Gain university degree
17. Pass (of time)
18. Confusing networks
21. Fatigued
22. Yesterday, ..., tomorrow
23. Found

DOWN

1. Kayaking
2. Be disloyal to
3. Weight unit
4. Cipher
5. Worn away
6. Relieve
10. Await with horror
11. Person paid
13. Saved
14. Blinded by light
16. Cinematographer's apparatus
18. Baseball glove
19. Swing to & fro
20. Send by post

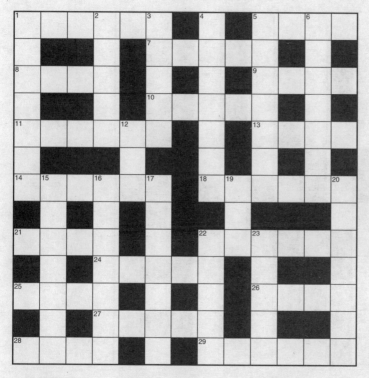

ACROSS

1. Messenger
5. Sketch
7. Furious
8. To ... it may concern
9. Unfortunately
10. Shockingly vivid
11. Pleasing views
13. Historical ages
14. Disorderly crowd
18. Valuable possessions
21. Cult
22. Called (of donkey)
24. Venomous snake
25. Solemn vow
26. Fir tree
27. Correct (text)
28. Eye droplet
29. Fish skin flakes

DOWN

1. Despite this
2. Allow inside
3. Radio control knobs
4. Hot spice
5. Numbs
6. Insistent
12. Afflict
15. Medium
16. Meat retailer
17. Made possible for
19. Knight's title
20. Melancholy
22. Musical groups
23. First Greek letter

CROSSWORD

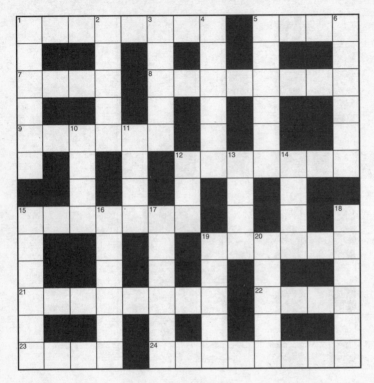

PUZZLE

5

ACROSS

1. One who solicits votes
5. Across
7. College test
8. Tidiness
9. Pencil-mark remover
12. Erroneously
15. Taunted
19. Rose high
21. Computer-based inventory
22. 100th of dollar
23. Watched
24. Rectified

DOWN

1. Grinned suggestively
2. Explosive weapons
3. Interior
4. Shocking ordeal
5. Possessors
6. Impetuously
10. Dull throb
11. Nobleman
12. Trend
13. Company emblem
14. On any occasion
15. Asian food item
16. Insist on
17. French pastry
18. Prepared (manuscript)
19. Locomotive power
20. Shorted

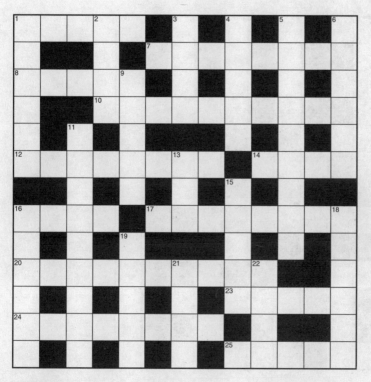

PUZZLE

6

ACROSS

1. Rot
7. Pool athletes
8. Of kidneys
10. Dilapidated
12. Originates (from)
14. Feral
16. Worry
17. Butcher's choppers
20. Limestone cave formation
23. South American dance
24. Green gems
25. Beijing is there

DOWN

1. Hold up to ridicule
2. A long way off
3. Nocturnal birds
4. Daub
5. Pocket blades
6. Climb
9. Tibetan monks
11. Sickened
13. Snake-like fish
15. Goes without food
16. More rapid
18. Musical composition
19. Lacking originality
21. Constructed
22. Every single

CROSSWORD

PUZZLE

7

ACROSS

1. Stifle
4. Praise highly
7. Window shelters
8. Little crown
9. Conceitedly
12. People taken from danger
15. Specimens
17. Pitiful
18. Interlace on loom
21. Marriage dissolution
22. Rogue
23. Loitered

DOWN

1. Restore
2. Using oars
3. Trilled
4. Compass direction
5. Gave therapy to
6. Flowing volcanic rock
10. Screams
11. Ribs to hips region
13. Dotted
14. Card game
16. Putrid
18. Candle string
19. Rim
20. Keen

ACROSS

1. Girl Guides & Boy ...
5. Imperial length unit
7. Satellite path
8. Paint roughly
9. Not here
10. Scent followed by sniffer dogs
11. Boxing hold
13. Eye membrane
14. Harm
18. Beauty queen ribbons
21. Immigration permit
22. Extracting moisture
24. Prepared
25. Piebald
26. Forearm bone
27. Golfer's two under par
28. Ancient
29. Places of interest

DOWN

1. Enticed
2. Of the city
3. Country, ... Africa
4. Acquires
5. Sloped writing style
6. Deadly poison
12. Gearwheel tooth
15. Originating
16. Gave (medal)
17. Trade boycott
19. What we breathe
20. Gestures
22. Dutch levee banks
23. Immature

CROSSWORD

PUZZLE

9

ACROSS

1. Upright
5. Pats
7. Street
8. Clutching
9. Rented
12. Climatic conditions
15. Deeply desired
19. Unrefined
21. Geometric shape
22. Citrus peel
23. Slip sideways
24. Spectators

DOWN

1. Masculine
2. Sea rhythms
3. Kept behind bars
4. Federation
5. Pill
6. ... & signora
10. Sector
11. Receive (salary)
12. Married
13. As well
14. Perceive aurally
15. Adolescents
16. Reimbursed
17. Puzzle
18. Interfere
19. Set of beliefs
20. Concur

CROSSWORD

PUZZLE 10

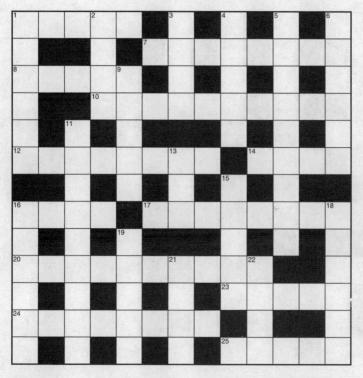

ACROSS

1. Talk
7. Expulsion
8. Sloped
10. Fearsome
12. Anything that
14. Departed
16. Dull
17. Courted
20. Significant
23. Domesticated
24. Tester
25. Rocky

DOWN

1. Unhealthily yellowish (skin)
2. Father's sister
3. Almost closed
4. Mock
5. Industrious quality
6. Horse-head chess piece
9. Native American tent
11. Twin-hulled vessel
13. Self-image
15. Entire range
16. Got rid of
18. Lethal
19. Legal
21. Mirth
22. Concluding

CROSSWORD

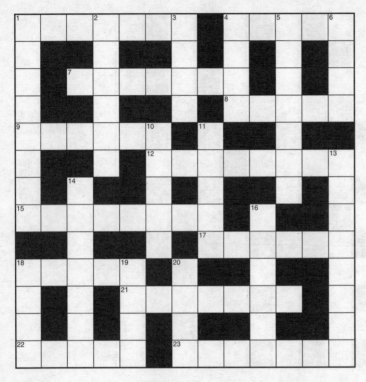

PUZZLE
11

ACROSS

1. Most heated
4. Dock
7. Pillage
8. Public square
9. Sewing yarn
12. Confectionery packets
15. Surpassed
17. Lessened
18. Way in
21. Citrus fruits
22. Classical musical drama
23. Foundry kiln

DOWN

1. Birthright
2. Conversed
3. Neat
4. Distort
5. Displayed
6. Hopping insect
10. Resided
11. Black & white mammal
13. Set of symptoms
14. Scurry
16. Pub
18. Resounding noise
19. Hindu meditation
20. Abandoned infant

CROSSWORD

PUZZLE
12

ACROSS

1. Slander
5. Strike with foot
7. Not tight
8. Small lake
9. Close by
10. Pixie-like
11. Food store
13. Tide movements, ... & flows
14. Jeopardy
18. Make certain
21. Round door handle
22. Degraded
24. Plait
25. Window ledge
26. Open mouth wearily
27. Sidestep
28. Tinted
29. Olympic throwing plate

DOWN

1. Pied
2. Lent a hand to
3. Older of two
4. Perplex
5. Dogs' houses
6. Room
12. Scrape (out a living)
15. Yearly stipend
16. Jabbered
17. Fugitive
19. Pen tip
20. Conclusions
22. Counted up
23. Deep chasm

CROSSWORD

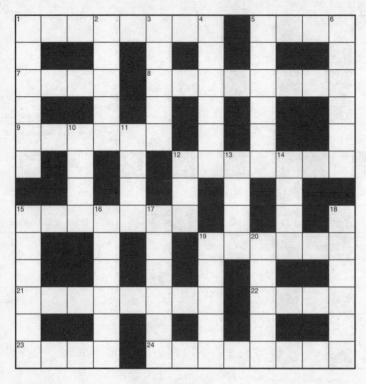

ACROSS

1. Most unpleasant
5. Minuscule amount
7. Front of ship
8. Reposition
9. Inborn
12. Concentrated solution
15. Freed of dirt
19. Oily mud
21. Policy of non-violence
22. Creative thought
23. Told untruths
24. Possible culprits

DOWN

1. Table linen item
2. Paris landmark, The Eiffel ...
3. Was incorrect
4. Long claws
5. Provoke
6. Take reprisals for
10. Wait, ... one's time
11. Equally balanced
12. Terminate
13. Aquatic mammal
14. Requirement
15. Urge
16. Joined forces (with)
17. Supplies
18. Sums up
19. Drainage pits
20. Amalgamate

CROSSWORD

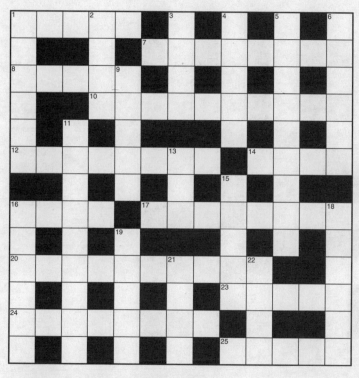

ACROSS

1. Person, ... being
7. Reposition (troops)
8. One-on-one fights
10. Environmental
12. Appreciative
14. Daunts
16. Lively dance
17. Beneath the waves
20. Autographs
23. Identified
24. Women's underwear
25. Scientist, Sir ... Newton

DOWN

1. Obscuring
2. Wheel spindle
3. Chiming instrument
4. Measure heaviness of
5. Wristwatch-hands direction
6. Recurrent periods
9. Spiral fastener
11. Saving from potential loss
13. Grecian vase
15. Number of days in a week
16. Bump roughly
18. Sharp-tasting
19. Estimated age of
21. Module
22. Sinks in middle

CROSSWORD

ACROSS

1. Natural (of food)
4. Leg/foot joint
7. Of the heart
8. Haul
9. Only
12. Canines
15. Immerse
17. High-gloss paint
18. Sailing boat

21. Oblivious
22. Stinks
23. Sniffed

DOWN

1. Road bridge
2. Astonished
3. Metal currency
4. Raise (eyebrows)
5. Worked (dough)

6. Fencing sword
10. Annual periods
11. Flood barrier
13. Scooped out
14. Vague
16. Keg
18. Belonging to you
19. Vats
20. Platform

ACROSS
1. Levels
5. Remove wrapping from
7. Fishhook points
8. Uterus
9. Inclination
10. Clergyman
11. Hinder
13. Plot
14. Drifts (into coma)
18. Served (soup)
21. Loose hair strand
22. Rang (of bells)
24. Stage
25. The ... of Capri
26. Number of cat's lives
27. Happen again
28. Invites
29. Job payment

DOWN
1. Timber-cutting factory
2. Easy pace
3. Superior to
4. Vital
5. Took (power) forcibly
6. Reduce in worth
12. Female rabbit
15. Pen names
16. Evening repasts
17. Wound with claw
19. Positive vote
20. Frail with age
22. Equals
23. Make void

CROSSWORD

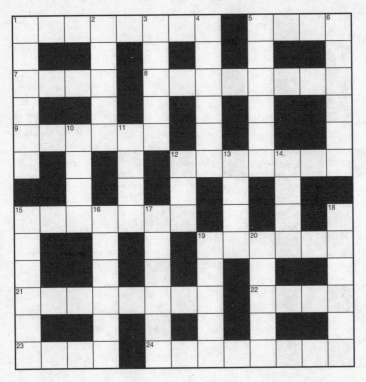

PUZZLE

17

ACROSS

1. Sleepily
5. Incapacitate
7. Vocal solo
8. Moved restlessly
9. Puzzling question
12. Headache remedy
15. Conflicted (with)
19. Legendary
21. Progressed
22. Male monarch
23. Parched
24. Scientific ideas

DOWN

1. Outlines
2. Introduces to solid food
3. Deduce
4. Sings alpine-style
5. Swiss cereal
6. Up-to-date
10. Greenish blue
11. Engrave
12. In addition
13. Cougar
14. Spool
15. Droning insect
16. Thread
17. Draw out
18. Maxims
19. Soft toffee
20. Bread maker

CROSSWORD

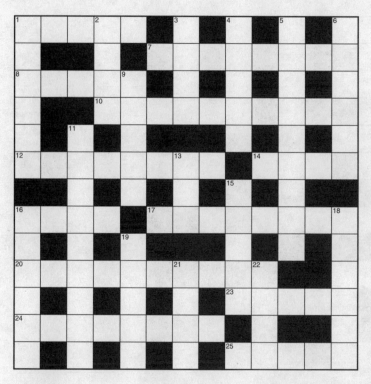

PUZZLE

18

ACROSS

1. Essential
7. Most humorous
8. Up to the time
10. Convalescent home
12. Grabs
14. Narrow
16. Swallow nervously
17. Cooking vessels
20. Newspaper's demographic
23. Underground molten rock
24. Movie outline
25. Nifty

DOWN

1. Crypts
2. Line of rotation
3. Surrounding atmosphere
4. Gold brick
5. Elated
6. Pollen-producing part
9. Gate fastener
11. Room decor material
13. Deer
15. Miner's land reserve
16. Gaudy
18. Unhurried (pace)
19. Tin or lead
21. Slithered
22. Sudden pain

CROSSWORD

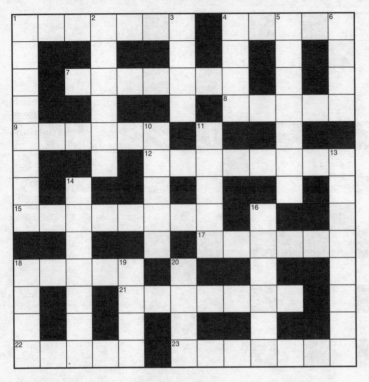

ACROSS

1. Hospital career
4. Before expected
7. Property size
8. Roves
9. Befuddled
12. Restate (position)
15. Sword holder
17. Gives way
18. Underground worker
21. Word conundrum
22. Personal glory
23. Poisoning by fumes

DOWN

1. Tells
2. Reaping blade
3. Objective
4. Pitcher
5. Despoils
6. Barks shrilly
10. Nightmare, bad ...
11. Behind schedule
13. Unquestioning
14. Portrayed in oils
16. Foot levers
18. Member of religious order
19. Knocks sharply
20. Group of workmen

ACROSS

1. Shock absorber
5. New Orleans music
7. Shrub border
8. Actor, ... Baldwin
9. Military equipment
10. Wall fresco
11. Undergo change
13. Overlook
14. Italian sausage
18. Abstain (from)
21. Cradle

22. Discontinued
24. Become liable for
25. Smile
26. Body of ship
27. Overweight
28. Has to repay
29. Muse

DOWN

1. Dam-building creatures
2. Central (point)
3. Nursery verse

4. Decorated
5. Enviously resentful
6. Walking corpses
12. Pep
15. Flight staff
16. Pure white animals
17. Frozen drops
19. Preceding day
20. Small child
22. Move stealthily
23. Pale

CROSSWORD

ACROSS

1. Revenue earning cargoes
5. Generous
7. Flightless New Zealand bird
8. Theatrical
9. Park warden
12. Table-top support
15. Changing room
19. TV reception pole
21. Moving (hips)
22. Twist in hose
23. Blocks (river)
24. Greatly enjoyed

DOWN

1. Embers stirrers
2. Reclining
3. Viper
4. Ice performer
5. Australian marsupials
6. Ten years
10. Insensible
11. Heroic tale
12. Golf-driving mound
13. If not, or ...
14. Move on tarmac
15. Scratched
16. Reflections
17. Less industrious
18. Satisfied (thirst)
19. Guardian spirit
20. Lawn tools

ACROSS

1. Formal arguments
4. Hot water burn
7. Invoice
8. Sober
9. Smoothed (wood)
12. Speeches
15. Rush headlong (of herd)
17. Subtle shade of meaning
18. Discharged gun
21. Unstable
22. Bears in mind
23. Scribbled absent-mindedly

DOWN

1. Syrian capital
2. Shopping corridor
3. Spurn
4. Congeals
5. Pilot
6. Action
10. Gives medicine to
11. Consumed
13. Yelled
14. String-knotting art
16. Barred
18. Marine creature
19. Adds soundtrack to
20. Took advantage of

CROSSWORD

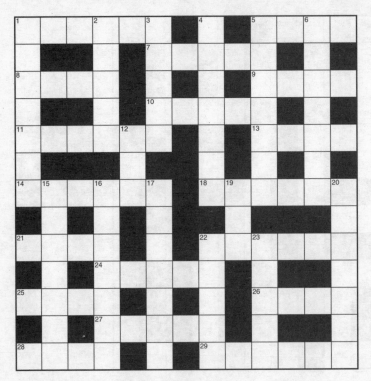

ACROSS

1. Highest point
5. Calf meat
7. Cousin's father
8. Ellipse
9. Ensuing
10. Personality feature
11. Language characteristics
13. Atop
14. Vehicle depot
18. Not casual (attire)
21. Roman robe
22. Requiring little skill
24. Watery-eyed
25. Wan
26. Perform again
27. Goat mammary gland
28. Guided inspection
29. Snake sounds

DOWN

1. Going fast
2. Arctic shelter
3. Feels sore
4. Grated
5. Undertaking
6. Worried
12. Large cup
15. Green fruit
16. Unpaid sportsman
17. Small chores
19. Caviar
20. Daffodil shades
22. One of the Magi's gifts
23. Standards

ACROSS

1. Undisputed
5. Irritation
7. Artist's naked model
8. Personifies
9. More taut
12. Ushers
15. Loss of memory
19. Painters' stands
21. Pilfering
22. Likable
23. Figures
24. Enhances

DOWN

1. Intricately decorated
2. Coral shipping hazards
3. Actress, ... Garson
4. Underground stems
5. Blue-violet
6. Silences
10. Sign-light gas
11. Large Australian birds
12. Period of time
13. Havana is there
14. Motorist's fury, road ...
15. Mistreats
16. Compositions
17. Strike (match)
18. Estimate (damages)
19. Enthusiastic
20. Of sound

CROSSWORD

ACROSS
1. Monarchy
4. Tough trousers
7. Very small
8. Do business
9. Drove (cattle)
12. Vulnerability
15. Sailor
17. Radio crackle
18. More senior
21. Without weapons

22. Draught beast harnesses
23. Holds to ransom

DOWN
1. Chef's domains
2. Gnashes (teeth)
3. Office circular
4. Forsake at altar
5. Mortified
6. Cash transaction

10. Old, cool star, red ...
11. Scalp strands
13. Yields
14. Field
16. Underground hollow
18. Whirlpool
19. Sprints
20. Blemish

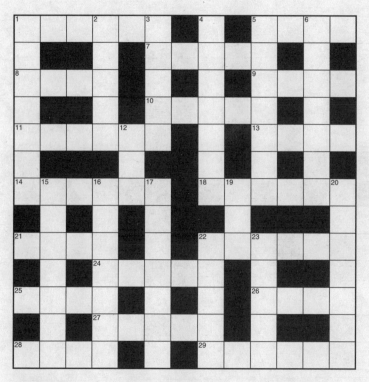

ACROSS

1. Mauve flowers
5. Object
7. Candle strings
8. Among
9. Muscat is there
10. Collar fold
11. Soup legume
13. Wartime friend
14. Ability
18. Disinclined
21. Applaud
22. Cloth
24. Yellow shade
25. Squash (insect)
26. Car (industry)
27. Leads
28. Nervous
29. Band of minstrels

DOWN

1. Printed handout
2. Accounts check
3. Expand
4. Shoulder blade
5. Seclude
6. Entitles
12. Charged atom
15. Permitted
16. Sympathy
17. Port working vessel
19. By that route
20. Wrap
22. Frozen dew
23. Pilot's code for B

CROSSWORD

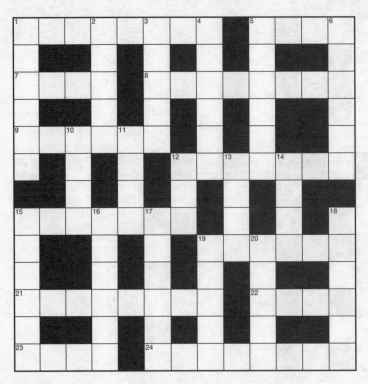

ACROSS
1. Striking difference
5. Fervent prayer
7. Not fast
8. Fearless
9. Hire contracts
12. Overlook
15. Grapple
19. Rural
21. Announced
22. Raise (children)
23. Paddy crop
24. Sun shower arcs

DOWN
1. Fortress
2. Communities
3. Touches at one end
4. Hypnotic state
5. Package
6. Kidnap
10. AM, ... meridiem
11. Revise
12. Formerly named
13. Hindu teacher
14. Departure
15. Shrivel
16. Geometric shape
17. Noisier
18. Rejects with contempt
19. Diameter halves
20. Clean by rubbing hard

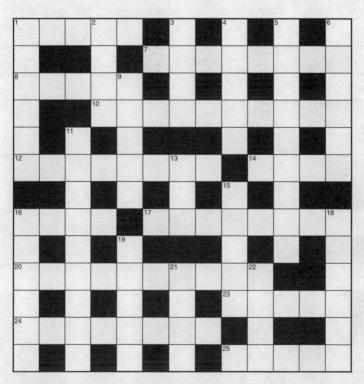

ACROSS
1. Sway suddenly
7. Fracture
8. Reflect light
10. Musical instrument
12. Tested
14. On an occasion
16. Rowing aids
17. Incited to action
20. Castle moat crossing
23. Skin sensor
24. Covertly
25. Reserve, set ...

DOWN
1. Bean or pea
2. Winter garment
3. Crustacean with nippers
4. Information item
5. Tolerantly
6. Flow back
9. Sorcery
11. Female family head
13. Deciduous tree
15. Pretend
16. Greatest in age
18. Remove (from text)
19. London's Westminster ...
21. Troubles
22. Snake-like fish

CROSSWORD

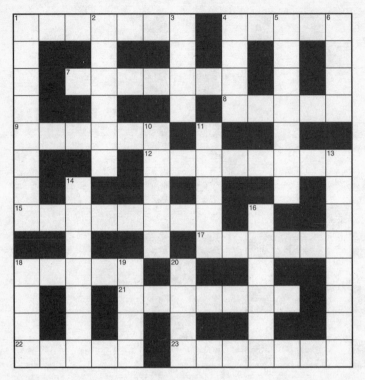

PUZZLE
29

ACROSS
1. Char
4. Backless sofa
7. Storing charge
8. Intends
9. Effect
12. Constant
15. Eminence
17. Covered with cloth
18. Peruvian mammal
21. Acted in response
22. Zones
23. Matching up

DOWN
1. Smudging
2. Lemon or orange
3. Tidy
4. Judge
5. Thiamine or riboflavin
6. Acorns or cashews
10. Melodies
11. Facial hair
13. Resenting
14. Due for settlement
16. Job path
18. Tibetan monk
19. Circle curves
20. Table light

ACROSS

1. Common seasoning
5. Rhythm
7. Remove completely
8. Moist
9. Slant
10. Extreme
11. Counterbalance
13. Sea phase, low ...
14. Skewers of meat
18. Going on horseback
21. Collar fastener
22. Not transparent
24. Happen
25. Single article
26. Links game
27. Strange
28. Avid
29. Contrite

DOWN

1. Detachable lock
2. Plumbing tubes
3. Disprove
4. Colleague
5. Tardy
6. Leave (sinking ship)
12. Wane
15. Qualify
16. Stomach
17. Witchcraft
19. Scamp
20. Joyful
22. Instruction
23. Debate

CROSSWORD

ACROSS

1. Made flexible, ... up
5. Increased
7. Petty quarrel
8. Fluid seepages
9. Exhilarated
12. Scrapes (riverbed)
15. Reduce weight of
19. Regard highly
21. Satisfied
22. Poke
23. Bellow
24. Effluent pipes

DOWN

1. Written communication
2. Suit
3. Governed
4. Desk compartment
5. Assessed
6. Desires
10. Very eager
11. Radiate
12. Lair
13. Furthermost limits
14. Clarified butter
15. Not so much
16. Female calf
17. Ousts from property
18. Smear
19. Bequeath
20. Candle

CROSSWORD

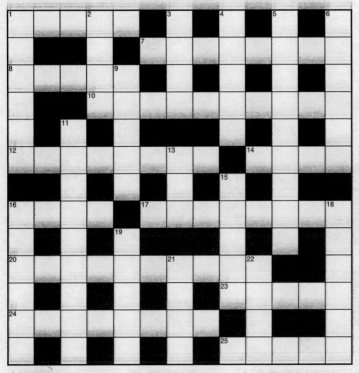

ACROSS

1. Regard smugly
7. Soothing lotion
8. Dull thumps
10. Unconventional people
12. Declare again
14. Author unknown
16. Bee nest
17. Rainbow's band of hues
20. Limply
23. Strands of threads
24. Passenger lift
25. Peculiarly

DOWN

1. Assemble
2. Attendant
3. Keep for future use
4. Social system
5. Idealist
6. Teaching session
9. Scrape (shoes)
11. Seeks (opinions)
13. Tear
15. Frostily
16. More sacred
18. Boggy
19. Church table
21. Wearing footwear
22. Enclosed area

CROSSWORD

PUZZLE

33

ACROSS

1. Of the Pacific or Atlantic
4. Contact
7. Hard to catch
8. Special skill
9. Meeting schedule
12. Religious dissenters
15. Average
17. Income cheat, tax ...
18. Exit
21. Promotional device
22. Complains
23. Murdering

DOWN

1. Fruit groves
2. In poor health
3. Front of jaw
4. Smell strongly
5. Stomach-settling medicine
6. Hind leg joint
10. To the fore
11. Rough
13. Boxing
14. Mosquito-borne fever
16. Scoundrel
18. Tower (over)
19. Farm produce
20. Go wild, run ...

ACROSS

1. Consult together
5. Stunned state
7. Fire fragment
8. Finger band
9. Affirm
10. Small notches
11. Eases off
13. Confiscated
14. Speared
18. Deceptive traps
21. Clean break
22. Develop into
24. Piano key material
25. Variety
26. Pledge
27. Cuban dance
28. Tallies
29. Tugged sharply

DOWN

1. Cut short
2. Boxing match
3. Horse control straps
4. Flee
5. Radical
6. Scientific study of animals
12. Poet's word for before
15. Pestered
16. Office duplicators
17. Twists out of shape
19. Facial feature
20. Fumed
22. Secondary route
23. Royal headwear

CROSSWORD

ACROSS
1. Divide
5. Large town
7. Piece of foliage
8. Nut-gathering rodent
9. Praises highly
12. Docked (of ship)
15. Titled men
19. Drew closer to
21. Minor dispute
22. Prepare (the way)
23. Bird of peace
24. Anticipation

DOWN
1. Blood-filtering organ
2. Terrible
3. Horse-like animals
4. Regard as equivalent
5. Orange vegetable
6. Shouted
10. Opposed to
11. Trades college
12. Commuter vehicle
13. Fragrant flower
14. Inheritor
15. Touched lips
16. Move in circles
17. Extended family groups
18. Stick (to)
19. Necessities
20. Orchard fruit

ACROSS

1. Common cereal
7. Craved drink
8. Planted (seeds)
10. Open to discussion
12. Illustrations
14. Insincere (of speech)
16. Envelop
17. Harsher
20. Shifting
23. Steam bath
24. Everlasting time
25. Inquired

DOWN

1. Squandered
2. Yemen port
3. Central US state
4. Intelligence organ
5. Steadiness
6. Verb modifier
9. Satan, The ...
11. Computer facts programs
13. Obtain
15. Occupies completely
16. Cricket bowler's target
18. Return to custody
19. Severe pain
21. Performs
22. Heads of corn

CROSSWORD

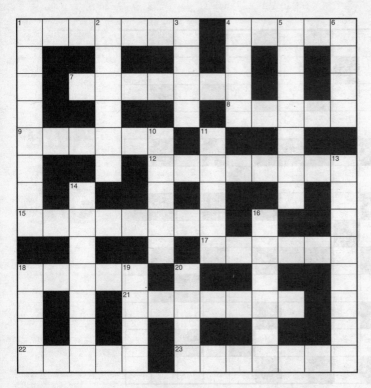

ACROSS

1. Living plant collections, ... Gardens
4. Spoken exams
7. Unlatches
8. Taunt
9. Journey
12. Jurisdiction
15. Glass fitters
17. Citrus fruit
18. Furnaces
21. French castle
22. Proprietor
23. Spanned

DOWN

1. Conducting oneself
2. Yearly
3. Lacking warmth
4. Unseat from power
5. Achieves
6. Profoundly wise
10. Fencing blades
11. Human trunk
13. Made beloved
14. Athletics field event
16. Risk
18. Greek liquor
19. Disfiguring mark
20. Post of doorway

ACROSS

1. Holiday memento
5. Mutilate
7. Inhale sharply
8. Shareholders' pay
9. Brings to bear
12. Easily
15. Layered timber
19. Bank cashier
21. Evident
22. Annoys
23. Head covering
24. False opinion

DOWN

1. Wrote name
2. Venomous serpent
3. Nodules
4. Withdraw
5. Spain's capital
6. Change
10. Jealousy
11. Musical threesome
12. Clown's prop, ... nose
13. Land measure
14. Cult hero
15. Deliver sermon
16. Sorcerer
17. Displease
18. Correctional institution
19. Add up to
20. Animal dens

CROSSWORD

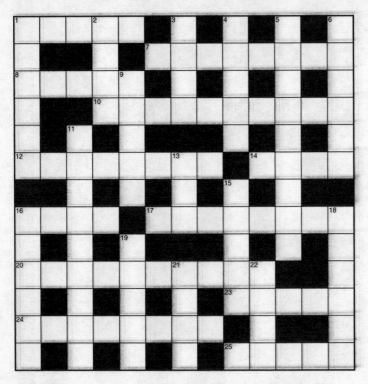

PUZZLE
39

ACROSS
1. World map book
7. Trilling
8. Fruit pulp
10. Dark outline
12. African or Indian mammal
14. Tiny insects
16. Regulations
17. Decreed
20. Sending ahead
23. Raw vegetable dish
24. Breathing out
25. Look fixedly

DOWN
1. Eagerly desire
2. Hatchets
3. Notes & coins
4. Concerning
5. Hearing, ... to
6. Concurs
9. Octet number
11. Fit to sail
13. Neither
15. Chess pieces
16. Raised high
18. Lag behind
19. Shopping complexes
21. Damp & cold
22. Manner of walking

ACROSS

1. Imagined
4. Woven fabric
7. Spanish rest periods
8. Guitar sound
9. Large lizard
12. Praises excessively
15. Absconders
17. Go aboard ship
18. Aviator
21. Improve in quality
22. Fashion
23. Cut violently

DOWN

1. Follower
2. Creature
3. Calendar entry
4. Knowledge quiz
5. Pierces with spear
6. Lengthy
10. Later on
11. Reason
13. Nauseated
14. Study of environment
16. Houses
18. Writing implements
19. Cylinder
20. Grows old

CROSSWORD

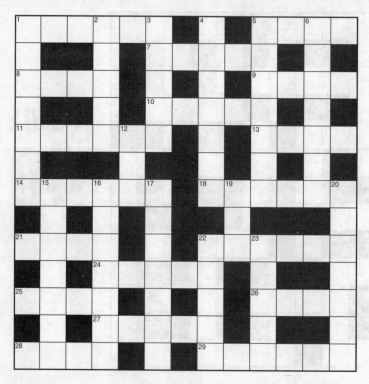

ACROSS

1. Craven person
5. Functions
7. Squares (up)
8. Rip
9. Radiance
10. Banish
11. South American vulture
13. Metal track
14. More effortless
18. Red salad root
21. Storybook monster
22. University award
24. Monks' home
25. Cure
26. Ride waves
27. Flax cloth
28. Reside
29. Humble oneself

DOWN

1. Fingernail skin
2. Ventilated
3. Adjourn to a future date
4. Convey
5. Escorted (to seat)
6. Choux pastries, chocolate ...
12. An individual
15. Supplement
16. In a perfect world
17. Stealing from
19. Top pilot
20. Attentive
22. Becoming extinct, ... out
23. Hearty enjoyment

ACROSS

1. Speaking indistinctly
5. Just manages, ... out a living
7. Female sheep
8. Sword sheath
9. Detest
12. Allows
15. Able to be heard
19. Unwind
21. Most remarkable
22. Outlaid money
23. Drove fast
24. Made stable

DOWN

1. Submissively
2. Surrounded & harassed
3. Magazine edition
4. Quick look
5. Preserve (corpse)
6. Moves furtively
10. Imitated
11. Parsley or mint
12. Pastry dish
13. Mar
14. Towards interior of
15. Straightens
16. Land enclosed by water
17. Defeated people
18. Flew without power
19. Disentangle
20. Got by

CROSSWORD

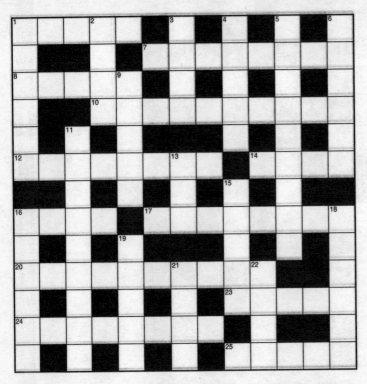

ACROSS

1. Work (dough)
7. Guests
8. Ancient remnant
10. Country-wide
12. Flowed out (from)
14. Faculty head
16. Hand-warmer
17. Abodes on wheels
20. River vessel
23. Food topping
24. Joined armed forces
25. Loose

DOWN

1. Japanese martial art
2. Similar
3. Suva is there
4. Keyboard instrument
5. Male law officer
6. Rearward (nautical)
9. Venetian waterway
11. Yellow bulb flowers
13. Historical period
15. Epic tales
16. Cleaned (floor)
18. Mouse noise
19. Poker hand, royal ...
21. Lost blood
22. Above average height

CROSSWORD

ACROSS

1. Sculptor's tools
4. Tropical fruit
7. Desolate
8. Unoccupied
9. Representing, on ... of
12. Trainees
15. Negative consequence
17. Formed
18. Implant
21. Foolishly
22. Setting
23. Rapped

DOWN

1. Disintegrated
2. Campaign motto
3. Reveal
4. No longer here
5. Modified
6. Sailor's greeting
10. Jumping parasites
11. Excursions on foot
13. Followed secretly
14. Leaf vegetable
16. Pungent bulb
18. Immense time spans
19. Feast
20. Wine vat

CROSSWORD

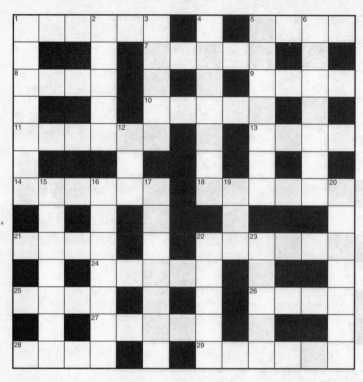

ACROSS

1. Escape vent
5. Deception
7. Conscious (of)
8. Grecian vases
9. Display frame
10. Trademark
11. Stamina
13. Curly-horned alpine goat
14. Word processor operator
18. Hours of darkness
21. Leak
22. Forward
24. Once more
25. Lyrical poems
26. Title
27. Velvety leather
28. Slothful
29. Lobs

DOWN

1. Luxurious
2. Light-ray tool
3. Brindled cat
4. Movable dwelling
5. Rounding up (cattle)
6. Archaic
12. Heating fuel
15. Bowed to the inevitable
16. Stalemate
17. Twisted sharply
19. Tavern
20. Makes unhappy
22. Beginning
23. Eye signals

ACROSS

1. More nauseous
5. Incendiary device
7. Had to repay
8. Granting
9. Aside from
12. Boasted
15. Glove material
19. Joined forces, ... up
21. Humanity
22. Male elephant
23. Small cubes
24. Steams in the sun

DOWN

1. Cited
2. Muddle
3. Improper
4. Harvester
5. Mattress pest
6. Beseeched
10. Printed greeting
11. Wolf group
12. Prohibit
13. Pimple condition
14. Low in spirits
15. Booted ball
16. Pacify
17. Bays
18. Grown-ups
19. Sample
20. Monastery superior

CROSSWORD

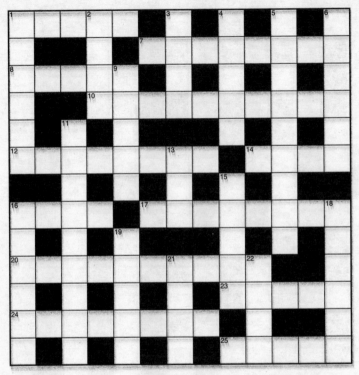

ACROSS
1. Proven details
7. Christian cross
8. Fend off
10. Desert gales
12. Longing (for)
14. Obligation
16. Hideous
17. Plan of attack
20. Witch's transport
23. Wading bird
24. Goading
25. Continually provided

DOWN
1. Rigidly
2. Neckwear items
3. Stepped (on)
4. Sharp (pain)
5. Offended
6. Has life
9. Turfed areas
11. Swelled dramatically
13. After tax
15. Third month
16. Become less formal
18. Sighed sleepily
19. More than sufficient
21. Huge amounts
22. Capsize, ... over

ACROSS

1. Come undone
4. Remain upright
7. Water supply tradesman
8. Put into effect
9. Delivery task
12. Re-evaluate
15. Scaremonger
17. Slithers
18. Doubter
21. Fateful
22. Encrypted
23. Walked like duck

DOWN

1. Rain shield
2. Not submerged
3. Experiment rooms
4. Positive
5. Grazes
6. Eat to slim
10. Sink outlet pipe
11. Ceases
13. Added spices to
14. Gibed
16. Fluid
18. Fashionable
19. Rope
20. Observe

CROSSWORD

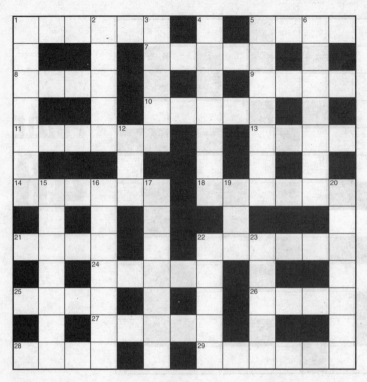

ACROSS
1. Render weaponless
5. Baby-bottle top
7. In need of scratching
8. Snatch
9. Wander
10. Add-on
11. Appeared to be
13. Timber fastener
14. African wildlife tour
18. Croaked
21. Wound crust
22. Concrete ingredient
24. Dog lead
25. Indian gown
26. Finish-line ribbon
27. Nook
28. Urban haze
29. Criminals

DOWN
1. Absorbs (food)
2. Soundtrack CD
3. Performed charade
4. Spread
5. Cruel rulers
6. Greed
12. Make slip-up
15. Recognition
16. Strolling
17. Early childhood
19. He is, they ...
20. Acts indecisively
22. Main
23. Motorists' inn

CROSSWORD

ACROSS

1. Dislodge (jockey)
5. Prolonged unconsciousness
7. Blacken by fire
8. Repaired (artwork)
9. Stage whispers
12. Affects with disease
15. Line of hereditary rulers
19. Japanese hostess
21. External
22. Pressing appliance
23. Nurture
24. Herb

DOWN

1. Unclothed
2. Bitter (taste)
3. Mends with wool
4. Naval flag
5. Preference
6. Examines (accounts)
10. Holy picture
11. Deciduous trees
12. Climbing vine
13. Front of head
14. Makes dove sound
15. Gobi or Sahara
16. Be present
17. Smaller
18. Mostly
19. Hindu teachers
20. Phrase

CROSSWORD

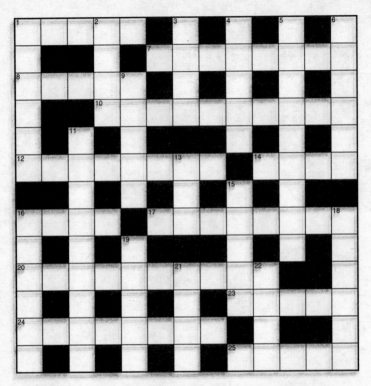

PUZZLE
51

ACROSS
1. Alcoves
7. Agreeable
8. Scold
10. Blessed
12. Twelve-month old horse
14. In contact with
16. Grizzly animal
17. Perfectionist
20. Sites
23. Beauty shop
24. Dazzled
25. Night sky objects

DOWN
1. Politely
2. Young goats
3. Power group
4. Glossy fabric
5. Bravely
6. Film production company
9. High-ranking lords
11. Job openings
13. Kernel
15. Feels sore
16. Roar
18. Boxing periods
19. Dismal
21. Long journey
22. Common seasoning

ACROSS

1. Burnt sugar
4. Reproductive organ
7. Swindle
8. Fright
9. Forceful request
12. Runt
15. Chained up
17. Moved from side to side
18. Of past times
21. Physical structure science
22. Military blockade
23. Sets of products

DOWN

1. Funny movies
2. Sports stadiums
3. Give temporarily
4. Gambling chances
5. Of water
6. Oxen harness
10. Reside
11. Female servants
13. Venice canal boats
14. Young pilchard
16. Airfield surface
18. Clumsy louts
19. Back of neck
20. Attire

CROSSWORD

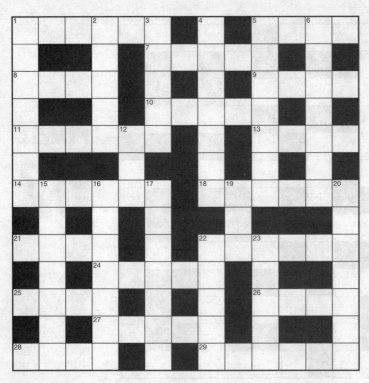

ACROSS

1. Phase
5. Shut noisily
7. Mental picture
8. Desert hill
9. Other way,
   ... versa
10. Sultana fruit
11. Finally
13. Travel on horse
14. Crockery item
18. Brutality
21. Kitchen
    professional
22. Flexed (muscles)
24. Tongue of fire
25. I was, you ...
26. Yacht canvas
27. Hurried
28. Service costs
29. Howled shrilly

DOWN

1. Sells on street
2. Awkward
3. Dirty looking
4. Processions
5. Cut off
6. Formally accepts
12. Untrue statement
15. Track performer
16. Money chests
17. Love story
19. Beer
20. Tampered
22. Elvis Presley hit,
    ... Bear
23. Of the nose

ACROSS

1. Climb hurriedly
5. Sudden invasion
7. Lamented
8. Clears of blame
9. Shuts
12. Magazine bosses
15. Stuck (to)
19. Seizes (power)
21. Serving ledges
22. Flowing volcano rock
23. Lose (fur)
24. Cause of mountain sickness

DOWN

1. Delivered (blow)
2. Helpers
3. Donkey calls
4. Followed on
5. Give in
6. Dance clubs
10. Pledge
11. On any occasion
12. Conclusion
13. Charged particles
14. On top of
15. Bead-frame calculator
16. Made (wage)
17. Inflammatory skin condition
18. Large property
19. Overturn
20. Dim

CROSSWORD

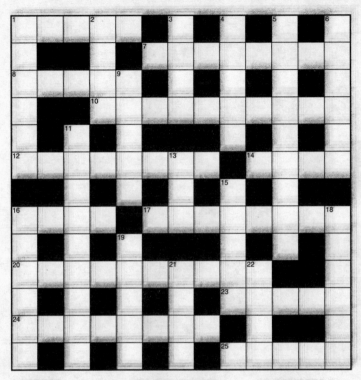

ACROSS
1. Edible organs
7. Denigrate
8. Female
10. Legitimately
12. Sketching (plans)
14. Widespread
16. Large cups
17. Wrenched
20. Kept in good condition
23. Beetle grub
24. Graceful style
25. Muslim faith

DOWN
1. Forward
2. A distance
3. Net
4. Petty quarrels
5. Male horses
6. Rewrite on keyboard
9. Half-way golf hole
11. Negotiated a price
13. Short sleep
15. Auctioneer's hammer
16. Associate
18. Deprive of guns
19. Weasel-like creature
21. Linear measure
22. Touches lightly

CROSSWORD

ACROSS

1. More durable
4. Leaving
7. Funny
8. Employees
9. Metal mixtures
12. Smartly
15. Earl or lord
17. Emerge from sleep
18. Makes joke
21. Public speech
22. Prod with elbow
23. Gain

DOWN

1. Herb, French ...
2. Frolic
3. Horse control strap
4. Concert tour bookings
5. Harms
6. Tennis ace, Steffi ...
10. Rascal
11. Hair dye
13. Most junior
14. Ashamed
16. Flatter
18. Connect
19. Single
20. Part of arrow

CROSSWORD

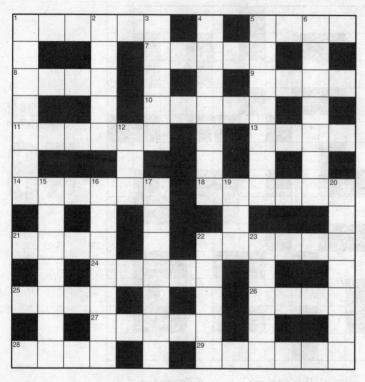

ACROSS

1. Glints
5. Fawns' mothers
7. Open wound
8. Actual
9. Of the mouth
10. Familiar
11. Lasciviously
13. Fleur-de-lis plant
14. Mexican flower
18. Earmarked
21. Rear
22. Portable
24. Fill with joy
25. Chopped down
26. Germination pod
27. Do well (at)
28. Looked at warily
29. Moment in time

DOWN

1. Incoherent
2. Became ill
3. Moody
4. Gymnast
5. Humming
   tunelessly
6. Test
12. Hawaiian garland
15. Dance
    school
16. Compared
17. Move forward
19. In the past
20. Greatly feared
22. Lunches or dinners
23. Elementary

CROSSWORD

ACROSS

1. Dangerously
5. Clay lump
7. Suspended
8. Mounted Spanish bullfighters
9. Probable
12. Regards highly
15. Burial service
19. Pursued closely
21. Wildly excited
22. Mausoleum
23. Lively
24. Show to be false

DOWN

1. Maintain (law)
2. Use fishing rod
3. Vacant
4. Sailing boats
5. Hug
6. Crockery items
10. Brick-baking furnace
11. Perjurer
12. Conger or moray
13. Bass brass instrument
14. Wicked
15. Flotillas
16. Of the soil
17. Waned
18. Fit for consumption
19. Sewn folds
20. Bury

CROSSWORD

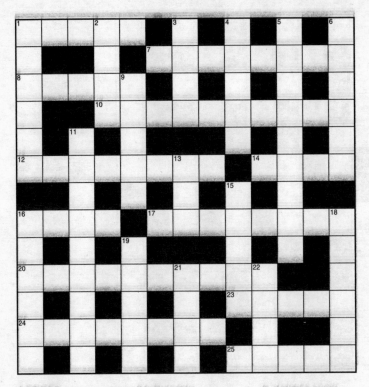

ACROSS
1. Percussion instruments
7. Propose for office
8. Bravery badge
10. Large hairy spiders
12. Sifted through
14. Did breaststroke
16. Camel's lump
17. United
20. Bulging
23. Three-foot lengths
24. Puts into bondage
25. Much of the time

DOWN
1. Fiends
2. Castle water barrier
3. Hindu meditation
4. Leans
5. Rolling (in mud)
6. Discarded cargo
9. Knight's spear
11. Rural residence
13. Sense of self
15. Black timber
16. Jumped on one leg
18. Small plum
19. Floorboard noise
21. Tinted
22. Fish-landing pole

CROSSWORD

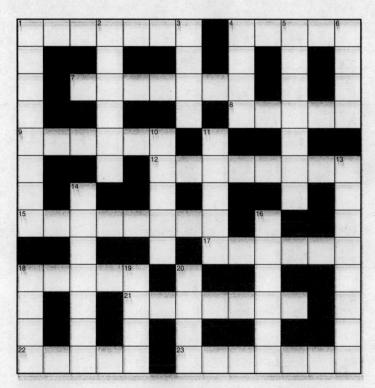

PUZZLE

60

ACROSS

1. Entangled
4. Prostrate
7. Small medicinal sweet
8. Leashes
9. Moves to music
12. Occasion
15. Ventured forth
17. Sitting down
18. Bookcase part
21. Refugee
22. Wood-turning machine
23. Entertained well

DOWN

1. Hepatitis symptom
2. Decorative pin
3. Dip into drink
4. Pare
5. Narcotic drugs
6. Large deer
10. Becomes submerged
11. Corrosive substances
13. Offered
14. Side-by-side
16. Photographer's tool
18. Dirt
19. Festival
20. Scalp growth

CROSSWORD

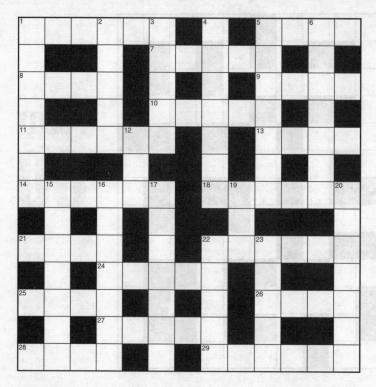

ACROSS

1. Mystery
5. Meditation routine
7. Classical musical drama
8. Rational
9. Flank
10. Educate
11. Feeling of revulsion
13. Postal items
14. Restaurant patrons
18. Trekkers
21. Rider's spike
22. Pure white animal
24. Alphabetical listing
25. Independent
26. Verge
27. Be merciful to
28. Ink stain
29. Four-door cars

DOWN

1. Perfume concentrate
2. Speculate
3. Main artery
4. Return bout
5. Muslim woman's veil
6. Dizzier
12. Tip of grain
15. Clothes
16. Weirdest
17. Garden timepiece
19. Out of sorts
20. Intermittent rain
22. Wheel shafts
23. Lose blood

ACROSS

1. Adopted battle formation
5. Wove
7. Forearm bone
8. Gaining knowledge
9. Removes completely
12. Crisp
15. Unkindest
19. Large African monkey
21. Relapses in recovery
22. Sketched
23. Perished
24. Blushed

DOWN

1. Extinguishes
2. Rests
3. Egg yellows
4. Desk compartment
5. 14-line poem
6. Cancel out
10. District
11. Lessen
12. Nocturnal mammal
13. Novel thought
14. Filled tortilla
15. Formed a crowd
16. Made insensitive
17. UFO, flying ...
18. Chewed like rat
19. Founded
20. Shift

CROSSWORD

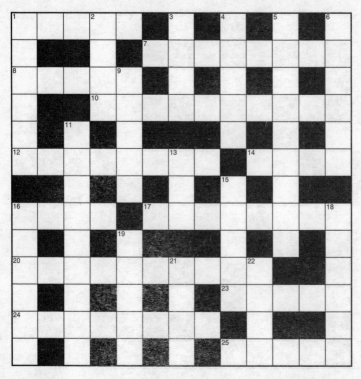

ACROSS

1. Skewered meat dish
7. Looks for
8. The same
10. Sixtieth, ..., eightieth
12. Stiffened (fabric)
14. Festival
16. Newts
17. Brings
20. Full-length
23. Outmoded
24. Skilled
25. South American mountains

DOWN

1. Works (dough)
2. Unfortunately
3. Measure (out)
4. Guitar-neck ridges
5. Footwear manufacturer
6. Respiratory ailment
9. Blood-sucking worm
11. Not wholly
13. Just manage, ... out a living
15. Pumped through tube
16. Explodes (of volcano)
18. Skids
19. Salty water
21. Antlered animal
22. Daybreak

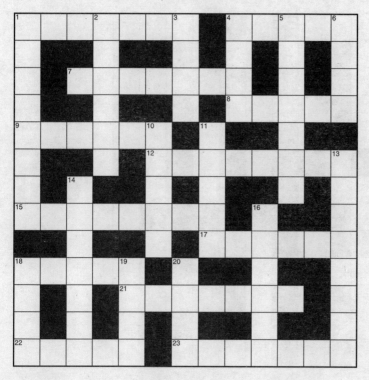

ACROSS

1. Unpredictable
4. Scorpion poison
7. Trainee
8. Bread-raising agent
9. Frozen peak
12. Flying around (planet)
15. Assess
17. Numb
18. Birds' bills

21. Defeat soundly
22. Kingdom
23. Avoiding (capture)

DOWN

1. Suitable (bachelor)
2. Office
3. Sugar source
4. Exceedingly
5. Wandering (tribe)
6. Edible flesh

10. White animal, ... bear
11. Waned
13. Crushing
14. Indonesian capital
16. Spoiled (of butter)
18. Brewery product
19. Plant stalk
20. Whet

CROSSWORD

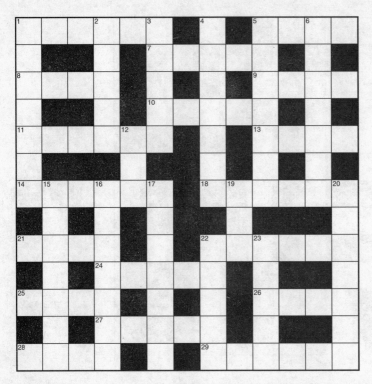

ACROSS

1. Let for rent
5. Cattle prod
7. Increased
8. Tiny amount
9. Not quite closed
10. Encounters
11. Except when
13. Warm up
14. Readily
18. Staid
21. Single combat
22. Zigzagged (through traffic)
24. Lower leg joint
25. Indication
26. Passport endorsement
27. Feasted
28. Spectacles glass
29. Fissures

DOWN

1. Relaxation time
2. Remove whiskers
3. Oil containers
4. Declares
5. Ground (teeth)
6. Inflexible
12. Spanish coast, Costa del ...
15. Offensive
16. Small land masses
17. Pulling
19. Mother sheep
20. Makes beloved
22. Unwanted plants
23. Blacksmith's block

ACROSS

1. Supplied funds for
5. Fencing blade
7. ... & papa
8. Tolerable
9. Containing bullets
12. Psychiatrist
15. Study of past events
19. Legends
21. Native American hatchet
22. No part
23. Bird's unhatched young
24. Perceives

DOWN

1. Woman
2. Hollywood prize, Academy ...
3. Cut into small squares
4. Mythical flying reptile
5. Tooth material
6. Excused (from tax)
10. Egyptian snakes
11. Reflected sound
12. Some
13. Radiance
14. Scream
15. Jostle
16. Court hearings
17. Respect, ... highly
18. Escorts
19. Forgeries
20. Spree

CROSSWORD

ACROSS

1. Breaks promise
4. Shake with fear
7. Gin cocktail
8. Period
9. Natural history building
12. Contested court decision
15. Lack of hearing
17. Grumbled
18. Letterhead insignias
21. Tanned animal skin
22. Submit
23. Trap

DOWN

1. Refurbished
2. Eluded (capture)
3. Large boat
4. Witty remark
5. Good-naturedly
6. Otherwise
10. Creator
11. Muscle twitch
13. Task-completion date
14. Luggage
16. Inn
18. Pond flower
19. Skidded
20. Evaluate

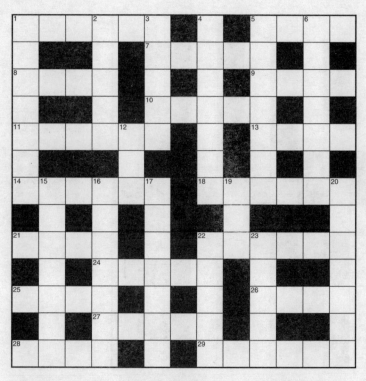

ACROSS

1. Squanders
5. Feral
7. Small crown
8. Belonging to you
9. Gap
10. Beyond our planet, outer ...
11. Over again
13. Coral barrier
14. Short pointed knife
18. Least polite
21. In a casual way
22. Wound (of river)
24. Slide on ice
25. Insignificant
26. Business note
27. Stands on hind legs
28. Invites
29. Withstand

DOWN

1. Ambushed
2. Concise
3. Hoard
4. Supervisor
5. Hesitated
6. Lingers
12. Observe
15. Postal destination
16. Hot water springs
17. Absconder
19. Large vase
20. Frog stage
22. Perceive
23. Pointed (gun)

CROSSWORD

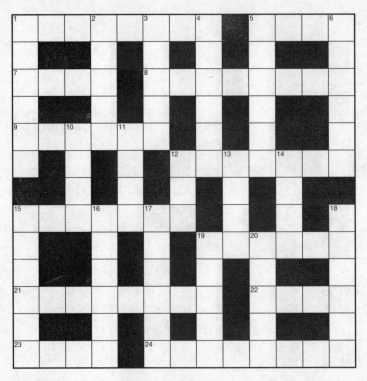

ACROSS

1. Soldiers on watch
5. Pig fat
7. Arm or leg
8. Dormant
9. Modern
12. Having whiskers
15. Young adulthood
19. More just
21. Meekest
22. Necessity
23. ... & duchess
24. Merited

DOWN

1. Income
2. Statistics chart
3. Simpleton
4. Sculpted figure
5. Last one
   mentioned
6. Ate sparingly
10. Infant's bed
11. Within range
12. Inlet
13. Singer's solo
14. Room opening
15. Shoved
16. Permit
17. Cotton strand
18. Exchanged
19. Destinies
20. Inside

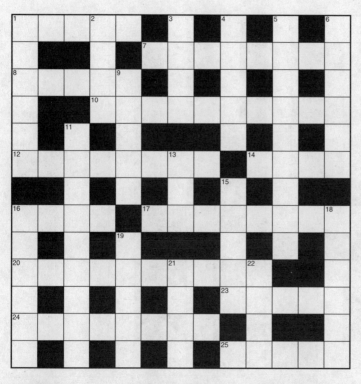

ACROSS

1. Fourth month
7. Got
8. Face disguises
10. Shrieking
12. Nonprofessionals
14. Beats tennis
    opponent with
    serve
16. Donate
17. Blocked from
    view
20. Bared (claws)
23. Subdued
24. Hand bombs
25. Established
    practice

DOWN

1. Fleet of warships
2. Printing fluids
3. Double-reed
   instrument
4. Livestock farm
5. Not genuine
   (sentiment)
6. Proverbs
9. Spiral nail
11. Gathered (crops)
13. Apply friction to
15. Group of eight
16. Resentment
18. Trawl (riverbed)
19. Lebanese tree
21. Foot digits
22. Water barriers

CROSSWORD

ACROSS
1. Befitting
4. Intended
7. Get ready
8. Australian marsupial
9. Enlarge
12. Resident
15. Stirring utensil
17. Fed on pasture
18. Communications industry
21. Without assistance
22. Middle
23. Tangled

DOWN
1. Army rank
2. Menacing warning
3. Take rudely
4. Humble, ... & mild
5. Predictions year book
6. Canned fish
10. Extinct birds
11. Freezing over
13. Twirled (thumbs)
14. Used oars
16. Merriest
18. Mutilate
19. Female relative
20. Dentist's mouth covering

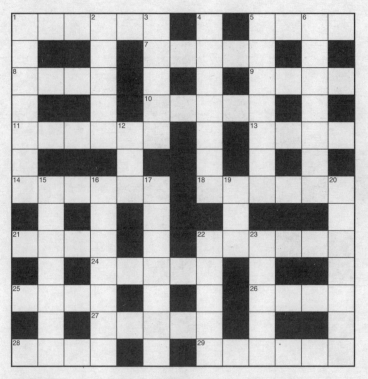

ACROSS

1. Fronting
5. Snare
7. Senseless (comment)
8. Long and limp (hair)
9. Sport squad
10. Feel with fingers
11. Positive electrodes
13. Saga
14. Barked
18. Plan
21. Word indicating action
22. Meet the cost of
24. Mild-tasting
25. Room divider
26. Cessation
27. Put in (data)
28. Table parts
29. Older people

DOWN

1. Mistaken belief
2. Irritated
3. Presents
4. Gave military greeting
5. Ties up
6. Astonishing
12. Night before
15. Par
16. Small round stones
17. Leaves
19. Folklore creature
20. Nodes
22. Worship
23. Manicured (nails)

CROSSWORD

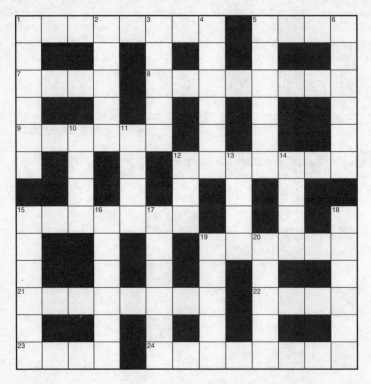

ACROSS

1. Respected
5. Dog parasite
7. Suva is there
8. Grow bigger
9. Fiction books
12. Compensations
15. Inundated
19. Heavily weighted
21. Returned to custody
22. Smear
23. Periods of time
24. Shake loose

DOWN

1. Filter out impurities
2. In existence
3. Water beads
4. Resolve
5. Spanish festival
6. Warns
10. Power of refusal
11. Noisy
12. Baton
13. Made on loom
14. Highway
15. Savage
16. Atlantic & Pacific
17. Gave off
18. Lacking the ability
19. Ore veins
20. Related to hearing.

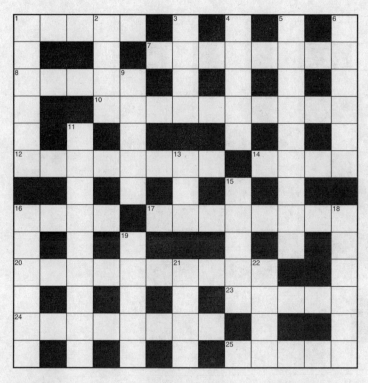

ACROSS

1. Body part
7. Imaginative
8. Around (that date)
10. Slept through winter
12. Water-landing aircraft
14. Courageous
16. Prevents from speaking
17. Obstruction
20. Wielded (sword)
23. Accumulated money
24. Physical activity
25. Peculiar

DOWN

1. Takes place
2. Curved span
3. Powerful need
4. Cautions
5. Invented (literature)
6. Repaired
9. Supermarket lane
11. Dialects
13. Zero
15. Area measurements
16. Window canopies
18. Worn away
19. Decree
21. Ornamental ribbon
22. Paris cathedral, Notre ...

CROSSWORD

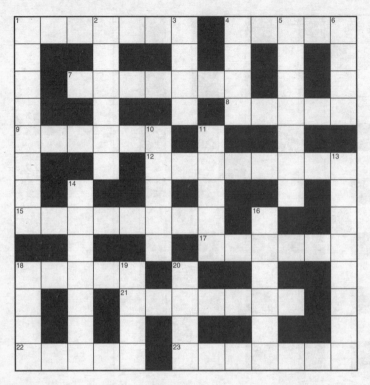

ACROSS
1. Chafed
4. Butterfly relatives
7. Seizes (aircraft)
8. Rogue
9. Expressed (opinion)
12. Dreamt up
15. Eagerness
17. Ten, ..., twelve
18. Glossy black bird
21. Citrus fruits
22. Wind-borne toys
23. Traipsed

DOWN
1. African anteater
2. For each one
3. Water bird
4. Type of deer
5. Despotism
6. Horse's father
10. Chops in cubes
11. Momentary misjudgment
13. Saturated
14. Domestic employee
16. Protect
18. Hazard
19. Assents with head
20. Floating log platform

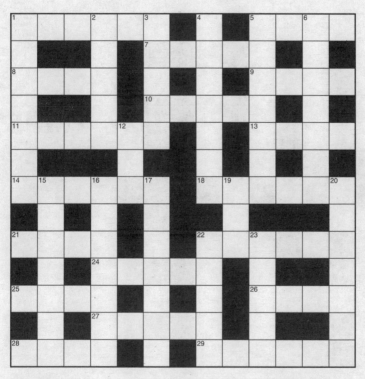

ACROSS
1. Completely
5. Hordes
7. Give speech
8. Tree anchor
9. Ridicule
10. Socially unacceptable
11. Entangle
13. Irritation
14. Cold side dishes
18. Engine seal
21. Match before final
22. Card server
24. Ruined Inca city, ... Picchu
25. Roman robe
26. Defendant's statement
27. Express gratitude to
28. Relinquish (territory)
29. In short supply

DOWN
1. Prison guards
2. Supple
3. Teenager
4. Catching (thief)
5. Autobiographies
6. Leg-powered vehicle
12. Piece of turf
15. Amazing
16. Enliven
17. Out of the ordinary
19. Mature
20. Row of houses
22. Water birds
23. ..., beta, gamma

CROSSWORD

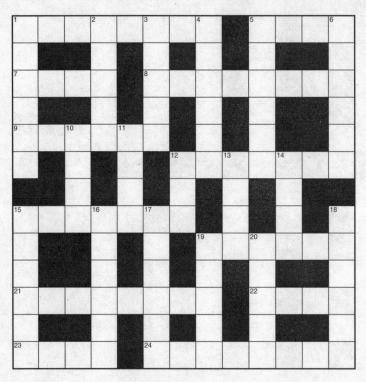

ACROSS
1. Incorporates
5. Clenched hand
7. Soared
8. Commented
9. Womb
12. Wine stores
15. Eighth of mile
19. Wedged forcibly
21. Enumerated
22. Desired result
23. Heavy metal

24. Miserable

DOWN
1. Flood
   (of visitors)
2. Bring down
3. Ventures
4. Word comparison
5. Ceremonial
6. Neatens
10. Large
    pitcher

11. Reverse the
    effects of
12. Gearwheel tooth
13. Tibetan priest
14. Nuclear weapon,
    ... bomb
15. Ship's chimney
16. Hit (ball) high
17. Slender
18. Confused
19. Arbiter
20. Sorcery

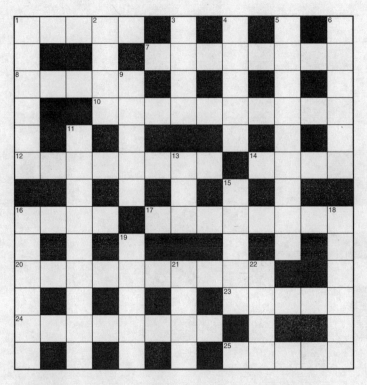

ACROSS

1. Weight measure
7. Fingernail care
8. Standard of perfection
10. Vitality
12. Epithet
14. Tie
16. Paper quantity
17. Complications
20. Arrests
23. Bird of prey
24. Richly
25. Beautify

DOWN

1. Source
2. Steamship fuel
3. Great dislike
4. Bridge designer, ... engineer
5. Adolescents
6. Stopped
9. King cats
11. Discarding
13. Spoil
15. Put up with
16. Cause
18. Partition
19. Fades (away)
21. Morays
22. Dune material

CROSSWORD

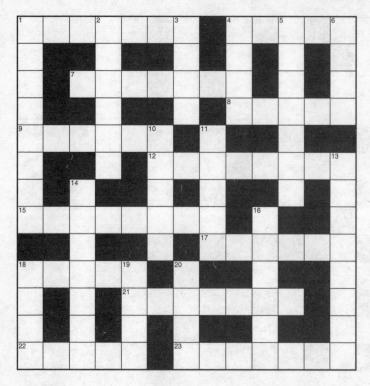

ACROSS

1. Rotated
4. Coldly reserved
7. Weapon
8. Long (for)
9. Trumpeted
12. Lacking compassion
15. News journalist
17. Subtle difference
18. Nimble
21. Awakening
22. Apportion
23. Touching with lips

DOWN

1. Moaner
2. Bird house
3. Radio knob
4. Force of troops
5. Natural (of food)
6. Young deer
10. Wipes down (furniture)
11. Oak kernel
13. Welcoming
14. Visual
16. Man-made waterways
18. Greenish blue
19. Opposite of west
20. Male fowl

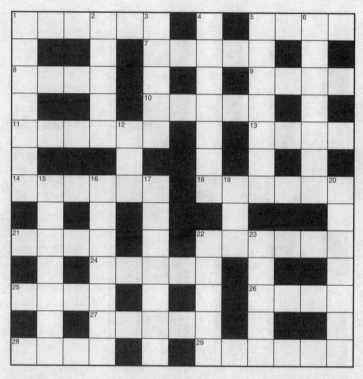

ACROSS

1. Raps
5. Tears
7. Garbage
8. US wild cat
9. Component
10. Pulsate
11. Undergo change
13. Absent
14. Italian sausage
18. Canine-borne disease
21. Rushed
22. Inspire
24. Guild
25. Not stereo
26. Palm fruit
27. Up to the time of
28. Allows to
29. Alters (text)

DOWN

1. Smoked herrings
2. Creep
3. Declare
4. Tribal fighter
5. Edible leafstalk
6. Gorilla or monkey
12. Vitality
15. Sanction
16. Strenuous
17. Demands
19. Rock band's sound booster
20. Couches
22. Father's brother
23. Cabin

CROSSWORD

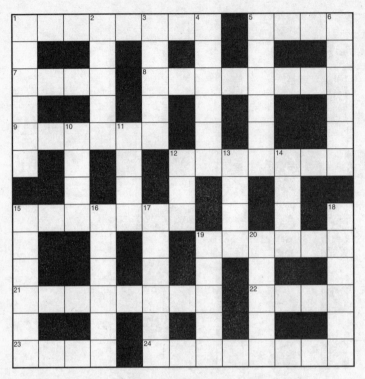

PUZZLE

81

ACROSS
1. Gun muffler
5. Hat edge
7. Small fenced-in area
8. Medieval farm workers
9. More leisurely
12. Epic journey
15. Allow
19. Pungent bulbs
21. Transforming
22. Handed over
23. Dispatch
24. Outlasts

DOWN
1. Most timid
2. Bequeath
3. Pickled bud
4. Bellowed
5. Fake bullets
6. Mental anguish
10. Neglect
11. Leave
12. Poem
13. Gape
14. Japanese-style wrestling
15. Casts out
16. Pressed
17. Sexual drive
18. Resources
19. Should, ... to
20. Silver bar

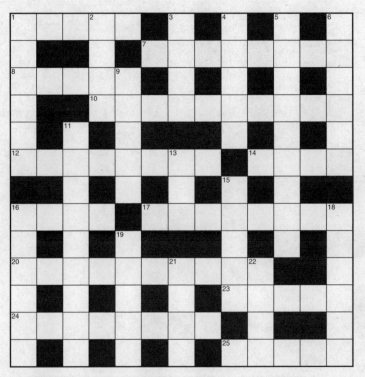

PUZZLE

82

ACROSS
1. Mauve flower
7. Gala opening
8. Unnourished
10. Colony
12. Disgraceful events
14. Dull impact sound
16. Theirs & ...
17. Sanitary
20. Ensured
23. Carried on (war)
24. Swap
25. Set of musical notes

DOWN
1. Chuckles
2. Gorillas or chimpanzees
3. Dry (of champagne)
4. Urge to action
5. Communication device
6. Spurted
9. Feats
11. Male family head
13. Produce (egg)
15. Ligament
16. Wild sprees
18. Rebuked
19. Deadly
21. Labels
22. Morse symbols, dot & ...

CROSSWORD

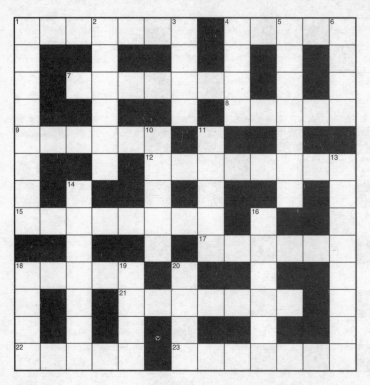

PUZZLE

83

ACROSS

1. Rise from depths
4. Get on (ship)
7. Flatter to excess
8. More liberated
9. Most recent
12. Large snake
15. Secret collectors
17. Looks forward to
18. Figure out
21. Thief
22. Tour coaches
23. Puts behind bars

DOWN

1. Strong point
2. Animal feed
3. School test
4. Cow meat
5. Insect feeler
6. Cheerless
10. Grabs
11. Light timber
13. Passenger balloons
14. Classical dances
16. Yellow fruit
18. Social bigot
19. Wanes
20. French cheese

CROSSWORD

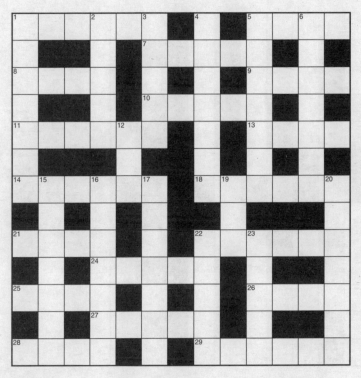

ACROSS

1. Sudden outflows
5. Chief
7. Lift with effort
8. Strong cord
9. Loop
10. Harsh metallic sound
11. Air strike
13. Frond
14. Ballroom performer
18. Reply
21. Body powder
22. Urging, ... on
24. Rest on knees
25. Let fall
26. Remake
27. Still
28. Leave out
29. Circles against current

DOWN

1. Musicals star, Judy ...
2. 'Laughing' scavenger
3. Trauma
4. Card game
5. Interrupts (speaker)
6. Stir
12. Billiards stick
15. Jumbled-word puzzle
16. Aircraft flight deck
17. Utterly fascinated
19. Old horse
20. Sectors
22. Exclusive
23. Injured with horns

CROSSWORD

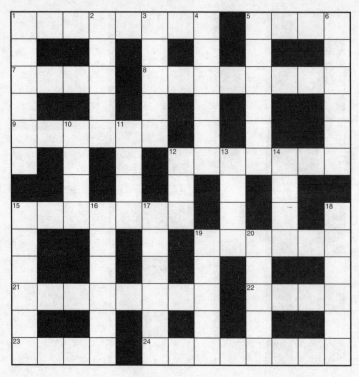

PUZZLE

85

ACROSS
1. Three-sided object
5. Anger
7. Small city
8. Trembled
9. Serving spoons
12. Dislikes
15. Responded to stimulus
19. Bible songs
21. Each person
22. Dress-up toy
23. Strike (toe)
24. Rainbow's band of hues

DOWN
1. Adds up to
2. Cancel (marriage)
3. Donates
4. Newly conceived baby
5. Display boldly
6. Sings Swiss alpine-style
10. Facts
11. Prepare for publication
12. Jar top
13. Ventilates
14. Drag forcibly
15. Readjusts
16. Angelic being
17. Print with raised design
18. Political refuge
19. Fragment
20. Examine (accounts)

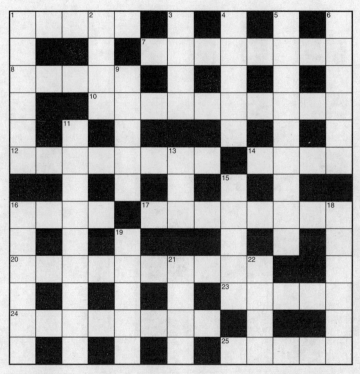

ACROSS

1. Imaginative plans
7. No matter what
8. Locate
10. Protects
12. Towed carts
14. Level
16. Crab pinches
17. Affixed
20. Opinions
23. National heroes
24. Improves
25. Snooped

DOWN

1. In one piece
2. Curving lines
3. Sandal or boot
4. Portly
5. During dark
   hours
6. Pencil-mark
   remover
9. Ahead of time
11. Small juicy
    red fruit
13. Groove in track
15. Spiny succulents
16. Bodies of
    warships
18. Drenched
19. Nutmeg or clove
21. Object
22. Wound blemish

CROSSWORD

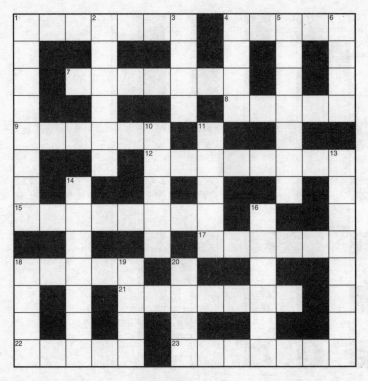

ACROSS

1. Amazon river fish
4. Dodge (duty)
7. Marched in procession
8. Shatter
9. Out of breath
12. Partaking of liquor
15. Technical sketches
17. Autographed
18. Plummets
21. Stirred up
22. Adult goslings
23. Sewing spikes

DOWN

1. Computer log-on code
2. Trophies
3. Counts up
4. Terminates
5. Stomach-settling powder
6. Apiece
10. Backless sofa
11. Chasm
13. Farewells
14. Retrieve (wreck)
16. Consented
18. Pull
19. Extent
20. Peruse quickly

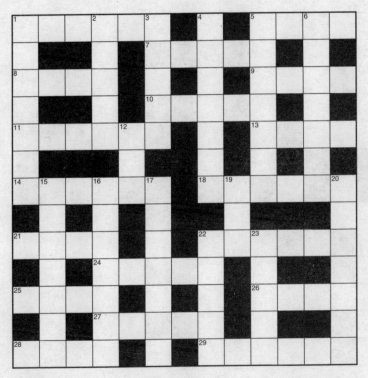

ACROSS

1. Involve
5. Labyrinth
7. Debate
8. Broth
9. Bound along
10. Boring tool
11. Guardian spirits
13. Portent
14. Crude image for mockery
18. Cease
21. Dressed
22. Funeral vehicle
24. Snow shelter
25. White metal
26. Group of three
27. Adjusted pitch
28. Farm produce
29. Inscribes

DOWN

1. Put into bondage
2. Orchard fruit
3. Touches down
4. Set fire to
5. Becomes gentler
6. Toothed fasteners
12. Air travel fatigue, jet ...
15. Making motion picture
16. Charges with crime
17. Shouting
19. Before (poetic)
20. Minor quakes
22. Multitude
23. Loft

CROSSWORD

ACROSS
1. Comes undone
5. Grow weary
7. Hawaiian dance
8. Lingering
9. More affluent
12. Laying off (one's bets)
15. Kept balls in air
19. Flattens
21. Sinew
22. Burrowing creature
23. Lowers (light)
24. Walked arrogantly

DOWN
1. Uninjured
2. Covered with water
3. Carnivore, meat ...
4. Restful
5. Attempting
6. Decorative border
10. Rugged peak
11. Fragrant type of tea, ... Grey
12. Was compelled (to)
13. Denmark native
14. Tiny island
15. Put in prison
16. Moans & ...
17. Surplus
18. Go up
19. Subsequently
20. Disgorge

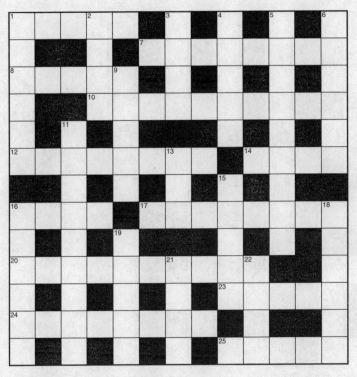

ACROSS

1. Yawns open
7. Flood
8. Enjoyed
10. German cabbage dish
12. Non-violent
14. Say it isn't so
16. Let out (shriek)
17. Calming drug
20. Self-appointed lawmen
23. Mixed (with poison)
24. Infuriating
25. Requested, ... for

DOWN

1. Horse pace
2. Optic organs
3. One time
4. Fork-tongued creature
5. Ambulance officer
6. Army camp lookout
9. Valleys
11. Feigns illness
13. Purpose
15. Humped animal
16. Resented
18. Escaped
19. Whips
21. Roman IX
22. Depletes

CROSSWORD

ACROSS

1. Massaged
4. Duck's call
7. Quandary
8. 52-week intervals
9. Summer or winter
12. By surprise
15. Rescued disaster victims
17. Concedes
18. Small pheasant relative
21. Golden hues
22. Taunt
23. High-spirited

DOWN

1. Remembrance
2. Between
3. Rounded roof
4. Dock
5. Matters
6. Vats
10. Unclothed models
11. Fizzy
13. Marine creature's home
14. Tropical disease
16. Margin of safety
18. Abandon
19. Ancient musical instrument
20. Hit with hand

ACROSS

1. Wisp
5. Bread rolls
7. Degrade
8. Radar screen spot
9. University faculty head
10. Dusk to dawn
11. Evoke
13. Freezes, ... over
14. Bicycle for two
18. Robberies
21. Ballad
22. Spanks
24. Cove
25. Wagon
26. Long narrative
27. Sports stadium
28. Highway fee
29. Hear, ... to

DOWN

1. Topic
2. Meat jelly
3. Intimidate
4. Most extensive
5. Sleep hour
6. Closest
12. Wrath
15. Tropical fruit
16. DVD, ... video disc
17. Postal workers
19. Cured pork
20. Maintain
22. Pilfer
23. Donkeys

CROSSWORD

ACROSS

1. Keep apart
5. Door handle
7. Pagan statue
8. Exults
9. Nevertheless
12. Cigarette end receptacle
15. Made do
19. Cows' milk sacs
21. Supported
22. Towards the inside of
23. Advance a loan
24. Pirates' hoard

DOWN

1. Coil-shaped
2. Enable
3. Assortment
4. Takes pleasure in
5. Titled man
6. Industriously
10. Knitting thread
11. Excited
12. Help
13. Contained
14. Ascend
15. Crumb
16. Fearful
17. Recruit
18. Onto terra firma
19. Uncalled-for
20. Uses towel

CROSSWORD

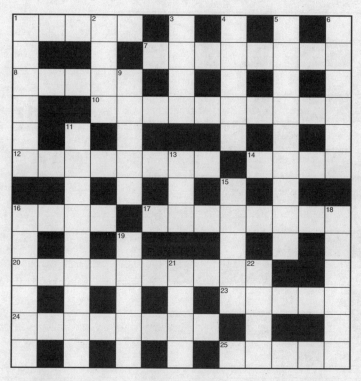

PUZZLE
94

ACROSS
1. Moist (fruit)
7. Foot soldiers
8. Cape
10. Pastry shop
12. Youth
14. Wild pack canine
16. Maladies
17. Very cruel
20. Paid profession
23. Totally demolished (of building)
24. Frozen floating masses
25. Wrote by machine

DOWN
1. Book cover
2. Applaud
3. Opposed to
4. Swamp
5. Ship's right
6. Me
9. Inuit canoe
11. Left untended
13. Historical age
15. Hate
16. Wryly amusing
18. Frank
19. Heavy fencing swords
21. Yanks
22. Admiral's command

CROSSWORD

ACROSS
1. Kept score
4. Ear test,
   ... examination
7. Unbeliever
8. Lodge firmly
9. Egg flan
12. Slimness
15. Novices
17. Deep shock
18. Small streak

21. Took tiny bites
    from
22. Paid out (cash)
23. More immature

DOWN
1. Calm
2. Madness
3. Failures
4. Wheel spindle
5. Rover

6. Electric cord
10. Imps
11. Girth
13. Unlawful
    occupier
14. African
    antelope
16. Cave
18. Current crazes
19. Entangle
20. Competently

CROSSWORD

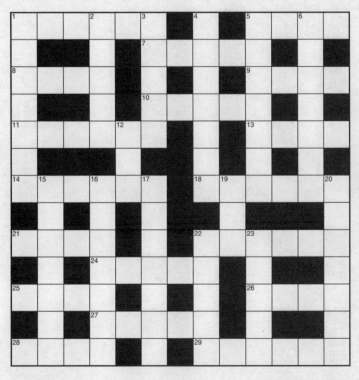

PUZZLE
96

ACROSS

1. Extracts (information)
5. Forgery
7. Large sea mammal
8. Actor, ... Myers
9. Horse farm
10. Bake in oven
11. Exalted
13. Annoys
14. Libel
18. Took notice of
21. Ewe's young
22. Crowd together
24. Edition
25. Daze
26. Pimple rash
27. Request from menu
28. Exercise clubs
29. Picks up (feelings)

DOWN

1. Placed bets
2. Vary (legislation)
3. Samurai weapon
4. Nasal discharge
5. Celebratory
6. Finger joint
12. Deciduous tree
15. Precisely
16. Pink-eyed rabbits
17. Part of a serial
19. Flightless bird
20. Weight watchers
22. Receives news
23. Attracted (to)

CROSSWORD

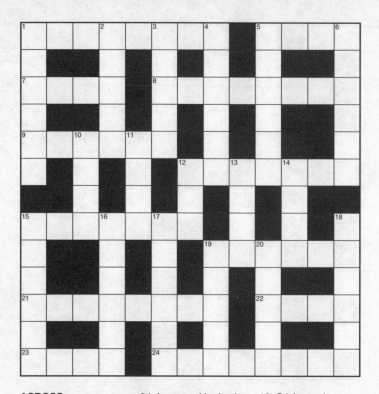

ACROSS

1. Miscues
5. Affirm
7. New Zealand bird
8. Warmed up again
9. Tidily
12. Caring for
15. Building caretaker
19. Human being
21. Whipped
22. Run in neutral
23. Cheese skin
24. Increased in depth

DOWN

1. Manufacturing
2. Dickens' novel, Oliver ...
3. Wed
4. Conspire
5. Astonished
6. Walking through water
10. Unknown author
11. Rob during riot
12. Sticky coal by-product
13. Facial feature
14. Taverns
15. Medieval king's fool
16. Decorated with set-in design
17. Exotic flower
18. Certainly
19. Army clergyman
20. Lift up

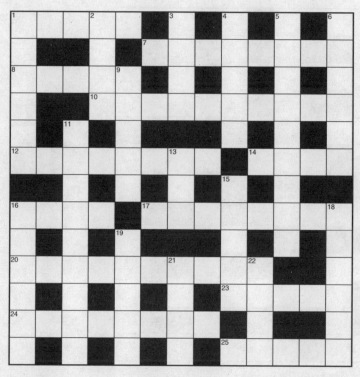

ACROSS

1. Sound
7. Dig
8. Throat part, ... cords
10. Sweating
12. Originated
14. Method
16. Render (tune)
17. Widens
20. Range of known words
23. Pulls sharply
24. Regretfully
25. From Japan or China

DOWN

1. Beginner
2. Trade
3. Discontinues
4. Proportion
5. Deep male voices
6. West Indian music style
9. Currency, ... tender
11. Shells on ship's hull
13. Slip up
15. Hirsute
16. Extreme
18. Add spices to
19. Regarding
21. Jaunty rhythm
22. Starchy tubers

CROSSWORD

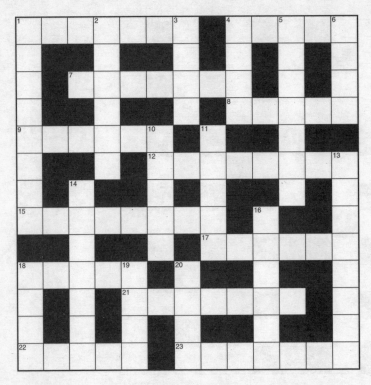

ACROSS

1. Scottish city
4. Ethnic groups
7. Held securely
8. Get to feet
9. Fooled
12. Re-emerge
15. Average
17. Radio interference
18. Blunder
21. Nauseous on boat
22. Soft & pulpy
23. Awaiting

DOWN

1. Pickled cucumbers
2. Non-liquids
3. Rub lightly
4. Purges
5. Wine vessels
6. Exchanged for cash
10. Horror
11. Hospital rooms
13. Salvaging
14. Lotteries
16. Speared
18. Dispirited
19. Catch sight of
20. Stinging insect

ACROSS

1. Remove pollutants from
5. Calf flesh
7. Corpulent
8. Grecian pots
9. Organs of hearing
10. Happen anew
11. Fills with joy
13. Wading bird
14. Shins
18. Muzzled
21. Metal in brass
22. Water boiler
24. Army fabric
25. Steel strand
26. Sponges
27. Regional
28. Grows old
29. Edged (towards)

DOWN

1. Destitute people
2. Map within map
3. Belonging to you
4. Using sword
5. Swerving
6. Aircraft company
12. Large antlered animal
15. Raining ice
16. US coins
17. Surface wound
19. Yes vote
20. Donned clothing
22. Exterminates
23. Easily frightened

CROSSWORD

ACROSS
1. Large tents
5. Uterus
7. Rework
8. Abating
9. Alpine melodies
12. Dairy cattle
15. Regimented
19. Sculptor's tool
21. Facial features
22. Was indebted to
23. Rescue

24. Hoarded wealth

DOWN
1. Sufferer for cause
2. Speech extract
3. Merits
4. USSR flag emblem, hammer & ...
5. Thick slices
6. Starts

10. Tinted
11. Lascivious smirk
12. Gladness
13. Hurry
14. Australian birds
15. Proposals
16. Allow
17. Page format
18. Oily mud
19. Indian social system
20. Cult heroes

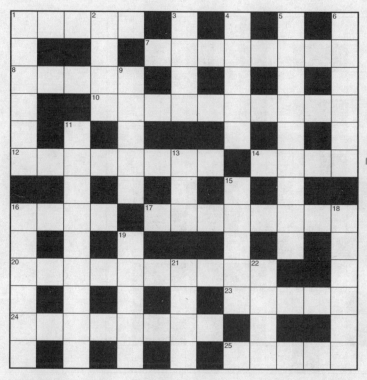

PUZZLE

102

ACROSS
1. Regional
7. Gently
8. Prompt
10. Cleanliness
12. Gripping (tale)
14. Prejudice
16. Tapering fruit
17. Flower sellers
20. Logos
23. Brazilian dance
24. Tidiness
25. Requested, ... for

DOWN
1. Fluid
2. Circle parts
3. Half
4. Perfect
5. Most intelligent
6. Laughing scavengers
9. Covered-in canoe
11. Twin-hulled boat
13. Unwell
15. Arduous hikes
16. Protect (invention)
18. Thread
19. College supervisors
21. In addition
22. Drains

CROSSWORD

ACROSS

1. Amazon river fish
4. Escape
7. Attack with missiles
8. Long (for)
9. Return to custody
12. Public speeches
15. Eagerness
17. Delighted
18. Every 24 hours
21. Citrus fruits
22. More senior
23. Looked briefly

DOWN

1. Tiny puncture
2. Lacking principles
3. Not here
4. Small whirlpool
5. Pilot
6. Smooth
10. Rounded roofs
11. Bring about
13. Made unhappy
14. Invigorated
16. Underground hollow
18. Drug (horse)
19. Belonging to you
20. Performed in opera

ACROSS

1. Consecrate with oil
5. Cut (grass)
7. Black wood
8. Opera solo
9. Did breaststroke
10. Circle (planet)
11. Examiner
13. Supplements,
    ... out
14. Plunder
18. Coyest
21. Petty quarrel

22. Go back on deal
24. Consumption
25. Be unsuccessful
26. Sound boosters
27. Tied (shoes)
28. Catch sight of
29. Dress ribbons

DOWN

1. Electric socket
   converter
2. Unsuitable
3. Male voice

4. Recreational
   activities
5. Suspense novel
6. Loom operators
12. Poultry product
15. Zoo inmates
16. Appallingly
17. Beautify
19. Shade
20. Locks of hair
22. Splits apart
23. Comes closer to

CROSSWORD

ACROSS

1. Brandishing
5. Festive occasion
7. Snatch
8. Protest posters
9. Young bird of prey
12. Book users
15. Rush of water
19. Small packet
21. Family member
22. Speed of sound measure
23. Paved enclosure
24. Emitted

DOWN

1. Shook (tail)
2. Luggage tag
3. Computer data
4. Type of beard
5. Chewed like rat
6. Corridors
10. Equipment
11. Rim
12. Decay
13. Region
14. Apiece
15. Roman XXX
16. Refunded
17. More inquisitive
18. Irritated the skin
19. Part with cash
20. Punctuation mark

CROSSWORD

PUZZLE
106

ACROSS
1. Leaves empty
4. Clergyman
7. Teach
8. Duck's mate
9. Panoramic
12. Show up again
15. Average
17. Twelve-monthly
18. Bad habits
21. High plain
22. Knowledge tests
23. Agencies

DOWN
1. Disappears
2. Counting up
3. Aquatic mammal
4. Competed
5. Defrauded
6. Ready to harvest
10. Floorboard sound
11. Cool Runnings
   actor, John ...
13. Reuses
   (material)
14. Eyelash darkener
16. Hunting expedition
18. Climbing plant
19. Health resorts
20. Ring of light

CROSSWORD

ACROSS

1. Orca, ... whale
5. Austin Powers actor, ... Myers
7. Move with effort
8. Without sensation
9. Nutmeg spice
10. Ultra manly
11. Whipped dessert
13. Curved-bill bird
14. Arrested
18. Pattern
21. Long story
22. Splashing (through)
24. Tropical fruit
25. Vampire's tooth
26. Shade of blue
27. Praise highly
28. Horse-breeding farm
29. Appeared

DOWN

1. Male relative
2. Fleshy parts of ears
3. Nursery verse
4. Emerged from egg
5. Autobiographies
6. Striking with foot
12. He, ... or it
15. Emphatic
16. Boasted
17. Leaves
19. Period
20. Miser
22. Room dividers
23. Hang loosely

CROSSWORD

ACROSS

1. More nauseous
5. Hawaiian dance
7. Run in neutral
8. Data entry pad
9. Touched lips
12. Accumulated
15. Lacking
19. Medieval maiden
21. Evident
22. Want
23. Fist
24. Took away

DOWN

1. Eccentric mannerisms
2. Helps (criminal)
3. Aggravated
4. Musical beat
5. Horse feet
6. Muddled
10. Summoned, ... for
11. Resound
12. Section of play
13. Charismatic glow
14. Is seated
15. Floral tribute
16. Announce
17. Straighten
18. Flew without power
19. Adored, ... on
20. Frantic

CROSSWORD

ACROSS

1. Adult girl
7. Sporting parachutist
8. Keep afloat, ... water
10. Strengthened
12. Revive (interest)
14. Salary
16. Orange seeds
17. Frying pans
20. Awfully
23. Spun threads
24. Infuriating
25. Pale with shock

DOWN

1. More damp
2. A distance
3. Alike
4. Colloquial saying
5. Cleared (war zone) of civilians

6. Hold tenderly
9. Ban
11. Small juicy red fruit
13. Deer
15. Cunningly
16. Army chaplains
18. Winter or spring
19. Proverb
21. Grecian vases
22. Shrill barks

CROSSWORD

PUZZLE
110

ACROSS

1. Card game
4. Hot water burn
7. Deflate (3,4)
8. Pituitary or adrenal
9. Message to run
12. Rate
15. Going by (of time)
17. Sailing boats
18. Leavening agent
21. Giving go-ahead to
22. Encore!
23. Imitating

DOWN

1. Coffee drug
2. Rinks
3. Go berserk, run ...
4. Hit parade entry
5. Predictions
   year book
6. Extinct
10. Jeans material
11. Pungently tasty
13. Surviving
14. Mosquito-borne
   fever
16. Barely enough
18. Hindu meditation
19. Pulled (of muscle)
20. Perfumed powder

CROSSWORD

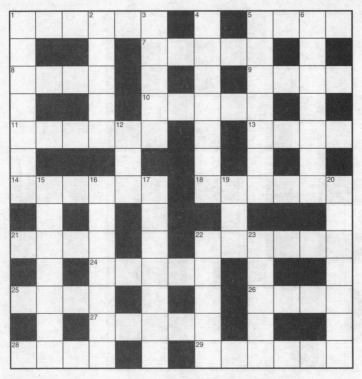

ACROSS

1. Large Galapagos lizard
5. Long walk
7. Actor's platform
8. Lamented
9. Become dim
10. Administered
11. Anybody
13. Freezes, ... over
14. Cold side dishes
18. Anxiety
21. Shove
22. Holy
24. Royal headwear
25. Lion abode
26. Travel along runway
27. Leading
28. Depend
29. Rail shunting line

DOWN

1. Encroachments
2. Of sound
3. Incidental comment
4. Perils
5. More weighty
6. Purifying organs
12. Bob head
15. Exalt
16. Cigarette receptacle
17. Lanced
19. Leaf beverage
20. Edging (towards)
22. Smooths (wood)
23. Mentioned as example

ACROSS

1. Answered back
5. Passport endorsement
7. Sell
8. Most fortunate
9. Stood on hind legs
12. Taunted
15. Royally
19. Lively horse gait
21. Small decorative object
22. Harness (oxen)
23. Prepare land for crops
24. False notion

DOWN

1. Wanderers
2. Greater in years
3. Laid slates
4. Decipher
5. Shrouded
6. Be present at
10. Highly curious
11. Fragrant tea, ... Grey
12. No
13. Large pitcher
14. Pork cut
15. Rebellion
16. Besiege
17. Folk tale
18. Lower dignity of
19. Blossom part
20. Gulf

CROSSWORD

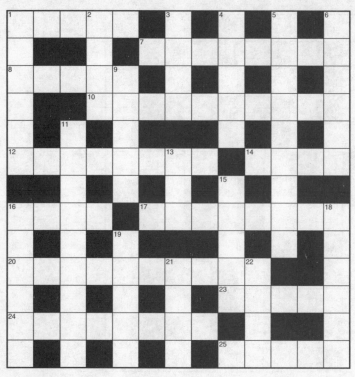

ACROSS
1. Skewered meat
7. Discharge
8. Tennis 40/40
10. Bicycle part
12. Sketching (plans)
14. Variety
16. Traditional wisdom
17. Religious doubter
20. Life history writer
23. Fertile desert spots
24. Courtroom testimony
25. Unbuttoned

DOWN
1. Tricked
2. Bridge span
3. In between
4. Valuable possession
5. Decisive match qualifiers
6. Unexpended
9. Our planet
11. Loyal to country
13. Scold persistently
15. Horse-riding show
16. Hit ball high
18. Hexed
19. Supplied with weapons
21. Agreement
22. Wet weather

CROSSWORD

PUZZLE
114

ACROSS

1. Coastal lakes
4. Copy outline of
7. Lost
8. Canadian gold rush region
9. Verb modifier
12. Not merited
15. Cattle charge
17. Emotional shock
18. Banjo sound
21. Sloping typeface
22. Marks as correct
23. Spanned

DOWN

1. Gymnasts outfits
2. Antipasto items
3. Fraud
4. Neaten
5. Emerges from sleep
6. Actor, ... McGregor
10. Consumer
11. Besieged
13. Left
14. Extremist
16. Spoiled (of butter)
18. Horse pace
19. Concert tour bookings
20. Post of doorway

CROSSWORD

PUZZLE
115

ACROSS
1. Border
5. Iridescent gem
7. Composition
8. Widespread
9. Put to the sword
10. Sugary
11. Cheap & showy
13. Concludes
14. Harm
18. Relieving
21. Ancient harp
22. Open wounds
24. Conservative
25. Weight unit
26. Evaluate
27. Riot
28. Give up (territory)
29. Bakes in oven

DOWN
1. Justified
2. Selfishness
3. Of topical interest
4. Inherent nature
5. Pearl-bearers
6. Leave behind
12. Small carpet
15. Whenever
16. Astounding
17. Involves
19. Afflict
20. Rubber seals
22. Cow mammary gland
23. Roughly (that date)

ACROSS

1. Ignite
5. Martial art
7. Formerly
8. Railway bridges
9. Conquering hero
12. Exerted force
15. Tom Cruise film, ... Sky
19. Classified
21. Explosive in nature
22. Tooth pain
23. Frog relative
24. Precious rock

DOWN

1. Gradually develop
2. Clumsy
3. Springboard athlete
4. Pencil-mark remover
5. Short excursions
6. Unseated
10. Maize
11. Ellipse
12. Pod vegetable
13. Always
14. Wearing shoes
15. Soft napped fabric
16. Set into surface
17. Existing
18. Cling (to)
19. Glow
20. Separately

CROSSWORD

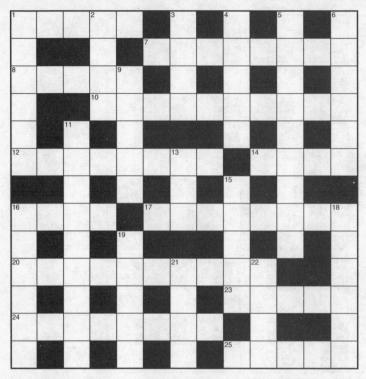

ACROSS

1. Adjust camera lens
7. Relinquish (claim)
8. Produce
10. Children
12. Custodian
14. Ballet, ... Lake
16. Canines
17. Devastate
20. Calmly
23. Adolescent
24. Islam or Christianity
25. Glided on snow

DOWN

1. Airborne
2. Unattractive
3. Blood vessel
4. Slightly wet
5. Lingerie
6. Teaching session
9. Not stylish
11. Hilariously
13. Mature
15. Poorly (lit)
16. Expel from country
18. Engraved
19. Pretend
21. Onto
22. Yellow part of egg

ACROSS

1. Small scrap
4. Listened to
7. Made duck sound
8. Pass into law
9. Male's partner
12. Cuts for examination
15. Circle width
17. Blood component
18. Cardiac organ
21. More tired
22. Wading bird
23. Grazing field

DOWN

1. Mixed up (card deck)
2. Singular or ...
3. Accept
4. Keep secret
5. Move forward
6. Musical piece for two
10. Prepares (manuscript)
11. Wrongfully seize (power)
13. Sit astride
14. Spanish bullfighter
16. Flair
18. Tall
19. Identical sibling
20. Sloped path

CROSSWORD

ACROSS
1. Changed into
5. Cook in water
7. Public square
8. Father
9. Speech defect
10. Lodge deeply
11. Urges into motion
13. Imperial length unit
14. Illness
18. Absorb (food)
21. Flightless New Zealand bird
22. More spiteful
24. Galaxy, ... Way
25. Volcanic matter
26. Noticed
27. 10 percent
28. At this place
29. Tendons

DOWN
1. Christening ceremony
2. Informed
3. Fencing swords
4. Played at, ... in
5. Losing hair
6. Six-legged creatures
12. Was ahead of
15. Stir up
16. Bring to life
17. Shouting
19. Wrath
20. Oppressive rulers
22. Folk tales
23. Incendiary crime

ACROSS

1. Fracture
5. Dog parasite
7. Burial chamber
8. Ocean voyager
9. Peru beasts
12. Disagreed
15. Untested
19. Japanese hostess
21. Military occupiers
22. Family war
23. Recounted
24. Was worthy of

DOWN

1. Conflict
2. Stamp book
3. Donkeys
4. Tooth coating
5. Banquets
6. Scared
10. Border on
11. Against
12. Atlantic fish
13. Competent
14. Weeding implements
15. Boost
16. Esteem
17. Surpass
18. Cushioned
19. Wind surges
20. Surmise

CROSSWORD

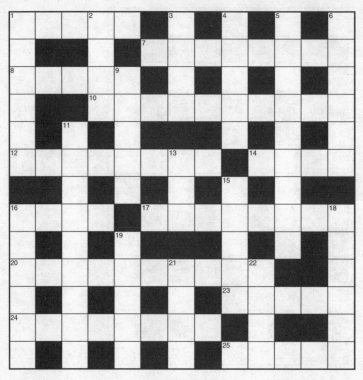

ACROSS
1. Wide
7. Ring-shaped
8. Curved
10. Storage buildings
12. Earl or lord
14. Fronded plant
16. Leave room
17. Jeans or slacks
20. Stalactite & ...
23. Steam bath
24. Hand bombs
25. Pilfered

DOWN
1. Spool
2. Once again
3. Tiny spider
4. Exclusive news
   story
5. Unnerved
6. Penitentiary
9. Palm fruits
11. Morally compels
13. What we breathe
15. Rifle ends
16. Naval flag
18. Fierce
19. Female title
21. Submissive
22. Compass direction

ACROSS

1. Disentangle
4. Give speech
7. Clap
8. Get up from a chair
9. International charity club
12. Resident
15. Wired message
17. Unmarried
18. Reproductive organ
21. Rearranged word
22. Unseals
23. Gathers

DOWN

1. Boxing blow
2. Request for aid
3. Amount borrowed
4. ... or evens
5. Stomach-settling powder
6. Ogled
10. Belonging to you
11. Illegal schemes
13. Ribbon awards
14. Wash
16. Unjust
18. Aware of
19. Tropical root vegetables
20. Tibetan monk

CROSSWORD

PUZZLE
123

ACROSS

1. Choux treat, chocolate ...
5. Angler's worm
7. Degrade
8. Havana is there
9. Air passage
10. Precise
11. Swapped
13. Fleur-de-lis
14. Spiced sausage
18. Took notice of
21. ... A to B
22. Piled
24. Prepared
25. Ancestry, family ...
26. Languish
27. Beauty shop
28. Hit sharply
29. The aorta is one

DOWN

1. Thrills
2. Hollywood prize, Academy ...
3. Scraped (leaves)
4. Nasal discharge
5. Nightly ritual, ... story
6. Slope
12. Horror film, A Nightmare on ... Street
15. In-flight attendants
16. Side of chair
17. In perfect conditions
19. Lamb's mother
20. Frail with age
22. 'Laughing' scavenger
23. Allow in

ACROSS

1. One million watts
5. Lively dance
7. Nourishment
8. Betrayer
9. Fills with joy
12. Dogs' houses
15. Happy
19. Puzzling question
21. Fisherman's wet weather gear
22. Empty space
23. Bridge-crossing fee
24. Sabotaging sprites

DOWN

1. Nursery rhyme, Little Miss ...
2. Financial records check
3. Awry
4. Chewy confectionery
5. Slang
6. Mistakes
10. Yemen port
11. Otherwise
12. Set of supplies
13. Nominate
14. Snake-like fish
15. Prance about
16. Glittery decoration
17. Taking notice of
18. Wears away
19. Mouth sensors, ... buds
20. Metal-working block

CROSSWORD

ACROSS

1. Fruit extract
7. Sauerkraut vegetables
8. Song of the Swiss
10. Sixtieth, ..., eightieth
12. Looks for
14. Facts
16. Male pig
17. Jointly
20. Car's night lamps
23. Art stand
24. Portable computer
25. Bereaved woman

DOWN

1. Cheerful
2. Snooker sticks
3. Japanese wine
4. Ease off
5. Pleasantly
6. Breathing disorder
9. Blood-sucking worm
11. Waterfalls
13. Flightless bird
15. Hotel apartment
16. At the rear of
18. Banana hue
19. Sphere
21. Increase in size
22. Sri Lankan robe

ACROSS

1. Nodes
4. Hornet relatives
7. Evasive
8. Room
9. Entertains
12. Low-ranked competitor
15. Desiring greatly
17. Radio interference
18. Attain
21. Expected
22. Hurried
23. Involves (in)

DOWN

1. Routinely
2. Except if
3. Pass lightly (over)
4. Troubles
5. Maroons
6. Footwear item
10. Not hollow
11. Male deer
13. Lifesavers
14. Zealot
16. Photographer's tool
18. Lion's call
19. Firm
20. Out of danger

CROSSWORD

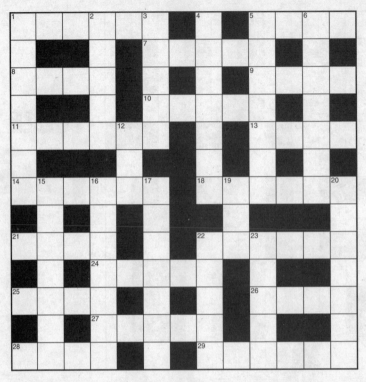

ACROSS
1. Nauseated
5. Imperfection
7. Fire fragment
8. Discontinued
9. At one time
10. Bird's perch
11. Washes soap from
13. Suspend
14. Speared
18. Brutality
21. Singe
22. Near-sighted
24. Native American tent
25. Actor, ... Hackman
26. Burial vault
27. Majestic
28. Used to be
29. Safe

DOWN
1. Argue
2. Assistants
3. Annual periods
4. Rectangles
5. Foamed
6. Climbs up
12. Supplement, ... out
15. Sports competitor
16. Funeral procession
17. Exhibit
19. Some
20. Gruesome
22. Fixes
23. Of vision

CROSSWORD

ACROSS
1. Elaborately
5. Storybook monster
7. Sacred vow
8. Crime against humanity
9. In short supply
12. Magazine issue
15. Deadlock
19. Pungent bulbs
21. Young children
22. Arm or leg
23. Skillets
24. Able to read & write

DOWN
1. Woodwind musician
2. Hate
3. Golfer's two under par
4. Pulled sharply
5. Of the supernatural
6. Ten, ..., twelve
10. On the summit of
11. Babies' beds
12. December 31, New Year's ...
13. Ferrous metal
14. Inside
15. Foot arch
16. Residences
17. Piglet's cry
18. Serviceable
19. Start (of disease)
20. Lazy person

CROSSWORD

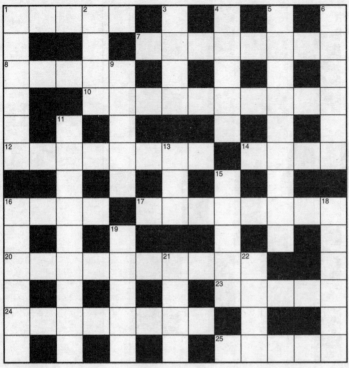

ACROSS
1. Peculiar
7. Explosive
8. Church table
10. German cabbage
   dish
12. Complete disorder
14. Visited, ... to
16. Thread
17. Harsher
20. Without
   commander
23. Destiny
24. Swap
25. Grind (teeth)

DOWN
1. Fluid units
2. Historical periods
3. Overblown
   publicity
4. Hessian bags
5. Connective
   tissues
6. Vanquished
9. Synagogue scholar
11. Female family
   head
13. Devour
15. Stall
16. Howled shrilly
18. Re-use
   (old material)
19. Spend time idly
21. Lower limbs
22. Hewn (logs)

ACROSS

1. Petty objection
4. Denim trousers
7. Green gem
8. Adulate
9. Mouth roof
12. Wanders leisurely
15. Extremely large
17. Warmed up
18. Connects
21. Showy-tailed bird
22. Unhappily
23. Shakes noisily

DOWN

1. Retorting
2. Bewail
3. College test
4. Beatles hit, Hey ...
5. Shopping walkways
6. Close
10. Devoid (of)
11. Wrist clock
13. Shivers with disgust
14. Set fire to
16. Lucky emblem
18. Glass containers
19. Desex
20. Wig material

CROSSWORD

ACROSS

1. Crustacean
5. Plot
7. Senseless (comment)
8. Power group
9. Goals
10. Of the city
11. Womb
13. Forearm bone
14. Bold
18. Cease
21. Curl of smoke
22. Grills
24. Charter
25. Very short skirt
26. Execute
27. Edit (text)
28. Henhouse produce
29. Opened mouth wearily

DOWN

1. Pacified
2. Become liable for
3. Religious
4. Talked incessantly
5. Charlie Brown cartoon
6. Oval nuts
12. Grecian vase
15. Enduring
16. Suggests
17. Parked undercover
19. Sense of self
20. Wrestled
22. Child's toy, ... bear
23. Crooked

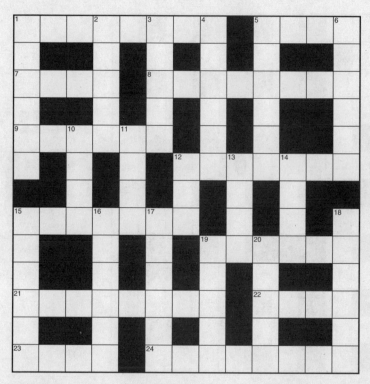

ACROSS

1. Living entity
5. Minuscule amount
7. Company symbol
8. Expresses excitement (over)
9. Shows gratitude to
12. Tampered
15. Retaliated for
19. Fused
21. Inhibit
22. Object of worship
23. Toboggan
24. Models of virtue

DOWN

1. Wise bird's chicks
2. Oak kernel
3. Objects
4. Intention
5. Accustomed
6. Ridiculous
10. Unit of land
11. Male monarch
12. Wet soil
13. Deceive
14. Tolkien's The ... Of The Rings
15. Burglar deterrents
16. Snared
17. Pitch tent
18. Confuses
19. Underground worker
20. Telling untruths

CROSSWORD

PUZZLE
133

ACROSS
1. Skulk
7. Enumerated
8. Wanderer
10. Ardent
12. Snatching
14. Money factory
16. Wither & droop
17. Decreed
20. Surmising guilt

23. Theme
24. Aptly
25. Frequently

DOWN
1. Longing (for)
2. Cover
3. Places
4. Head monk
5. Inventions
6. Most peculiar

9. Smears
11. Weapon, ... missile
13. Neither here
    ... there
15. Portray in oils
16. Shrewdest
18. Actress, Lindsay ...
19. Tin or lead
21. Slant
22. Fairway sport

ACROSS

1. Public plant park, ... garden
4. Australian marsupial
7. Mythical woman/ fish
8. Cloud of insects
9. Happens
12. Infidels
15. Snag
17. Unnerved
18. Scoundrel
21. Straight-faced
22. Rock and roll pioneer, ... Holly
23. Inhalations

DOWN

1. Fastened coat, ... up
2. Wide street
3. Overfill
4. Young goats
5. Assumed identities
6. Molecule part
10. Tied bundle
11. Financial institutions
13. Dutch liquor
14. Pillaged
16. Curved fruit
18. Handle
19. Nervous
20. Dress

CROSSWORD

ACROSS

1. Rock levels
5. Has
7. Bible song
8. Novel thought
9. Skin irritation
10. Acquire skills
11. Simply
13. Leave out
14. Moved rhythmically
18. Quit job
21. Swedish pop group
22. Cows' milk sacs
24. Fish commercially
25. Largest body joint
26. Yearning
27. Sharp crest
28. Invites
29. Warm up again

DOWN

1. Slid
2. Astound
3. Be relevant
4. Spanish bullfighter
5. Foreboding
6. Cutting with razor
12. Untruth
15. Pure white animals
16. Meteor impact holes
17. Forceful requests
19. Outcome
20. Most inquisitive
22. Mouth sore
23. Unbaked bread

PUZZLE
136

ACROSS

1. In these times
5. Jetty
7. Computer symbol
8. Leaves behind
9. Removes completely
12. Chirped
15. Disciple
19. Cured
21. Niftiest
22. Fully satisfy

23. Transmit
24. Hangs

DOWN

1. Secured by hammering
2. Female relatives
3. Collect
4. Follow closely
5. Pool of rainwater
6. Took a break
10. As well

11. Radiate
12. Film, Gone With ... Wind
13. Simplicity
14. What a dog wags
15. Spies, secret ...
16. Wept
17. Reduces
18. Vipers
19. Detests
20. Supermarket lane

CROSSWORD

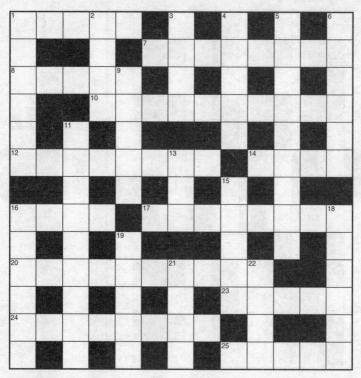

ACROSS

1. Board game
7. Smudging
8. Common
10. Olympic event, Modern ...
12. Giving up
14. Hindu exercise routine
16. Membership fees
17. Morally corrupt
20. Assured
23. Mends with wool
24. Strategic
25. Remained upright

DOWN

1. Inept
2. Click (fingers)
3. Overlook
4. Italian dish
5. Strength of mind
6. Meeting schedule
9. Advances (cash)
11. Pertinence
13. Formerly known as
15. Placed in an aviary
16. Numbers
18. Tightened (muscles)
19. Craze
21. Rip
22. Blowpipe missile

CROSSWORD

PUZZLE

138

ACROSS
1. Fishing sport
4. Mental picture
7. Disgraceful event
8. Hidden supply
9. Skin complaint
12. In the interim
15. Re-evaluate
17. Emerge from sleep
18. Immobile
21. Without assistance
22. Sidestep
23. Carried too far

DOWN
1. Successful person
2. Sea bottom, Davy Jones's ...
3. Deities
4. Misfortunes
5. Water-related
6. Inscribe
10. Fossil resin
11. Lightweight timber
13. Entrapped
14. Faltered
16. Job path
18. Frozen, ... over
19. Pipe
20. Mexican food shell

CROSSWORD

ACROSS

1. Unanchored
5. Destiny
7. Novel, ... Tom's Cabin
8. Respiratory organ
9. Calf meat
10. Subject matter
11. Rasps
13. Wealthy
14. Expel from country
18. Red salad root
21. Fifty per cent
22. Sloping (typeface)
24. Truncheon
25. Hint
26. Dedicatory poems
27. Cause laughter
28. Revise (manuscript)
29. Candle wax

DOWN

1. Claimed
2. Gold bar
3. Bunches of feathers
4. Conspirator
5. Frenzied
6. Hypnotic states
12. Wheat tip
15. Entitled
16. Unconventional
17. Temper outburst
19. Astern
20. Cutting blade
22. Estuary
23. Ring-shaped coral isle

CROSSWORD

ACROSS

1. Came into view
5. Stroll
7. Perished
8. Plays the part of
9. Scratched
12. Great pains
15. Moves restlessly
19. Sounds
21. Comical
22. Antlered animal
23. Performed
24. Star clusters

DOWN

1. Kidnap
2. Bequeath
3. Swift
4. For the duration of
5. Deteriorate
6. Affectionate gestures
10. Eager
11. Fencing sword
12. Donkey
13. Greek liquor
14. Riles
15. Used hook & line
16. Channel
17. Multitude
18. Seizes (power)
19. Of the nose
20. Tabulated list

CROSSWORD

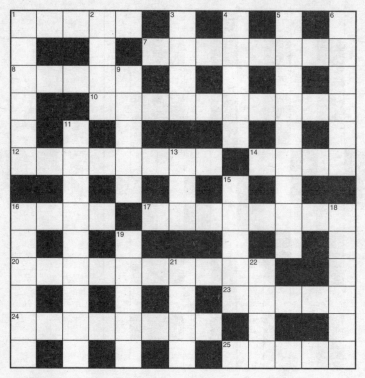

ACROSS

1. Skilful
7. Encode
8. Moan
10. Wantonly destroying
12. Nonprofessionals
14. Slide
16. Clock face
17. Detained during war
20. Made worse
23. Immature insect
24. US president, ... Roosevelt
25. Not these but ...

DOWN

1. Heart pain
2. Whistle balls
3. Open (parcel)
4. Travel permits
5. Screeching
6. Unresponsive
9. Type of orange
11. Shouts at
13. Jog
15. Resist authority
16. Rough plans
18. Widen (pupils)
19. Readily available
21. Askew
22. Hyphen

ACROSS

1. Leftover piece
4. Sentry
7. Steering mechanism
8. Dining bench
9. Mourn
12. Evilly
15. Boiled gently
17. Equine complex
18. Wine fruit

21. Muslim veil
22. Fills with air, ... up
23. Mislead

DOWN

1. Asylum seekers
2. Lasso loops
3. Make weary
4. Gold leaf
5. Anyone
6. Rounded roof
10. Large jugs

11. Corrosive substances
13. Christmas season
14. Official trade ban
16. Enchantress, femme ...
18. Insincere (of speech)
19. Detectives, private ...
20. Availed oneself of

CROSSWORD

ACROSS

1. Sea journey
5. Ocean's flow
7. Russian liquor
8. Verbal
9. Scolds repeatedly
10. Register at hotel, ... in
11. Amongst
13. Zenith
14. Deserved
18. Most aged
21. Banded quartz
22. Lightly touched
24. Very angry
25. Grain store
26. A selection
27. Dim
28. Pigments
29. Protective headgear

DOWN

1. Infringe (law)
2. Troubled
3. Legally expel
4. Negative (criticism)
5. Large beer mug
6. Short pointed knives
12. Seek damages from
15. Annual allowance
16. Poisonous
17. Failure to pay
19. Meadow (poetic)
20. Neatest
22. Fatality
23. Sweet herb

ACROSS

1. Orchestral composition
5. Animal foot
7. Small drop
8. Vacations
9. Expedition head
12. Stuck (to)
15. Angered
19. Made airtight
21. Deviated
22. Dinner chime
23. Retailed
24. Frees from blame

DOWN

1. Jockey's seat
2. Pumped through tube
3. Alternate
4. Shouted
5. Crowd together
6. Abstained from food
10. Actor, ... Alda
11. Effortless
12. Also
13. Possess
14. Fishing spool
15. Incidental comments
16. Insult
17. Puzzle
18. Proverbs
19. Sports teams
20. Protector, guardian ...

CROSSWORD

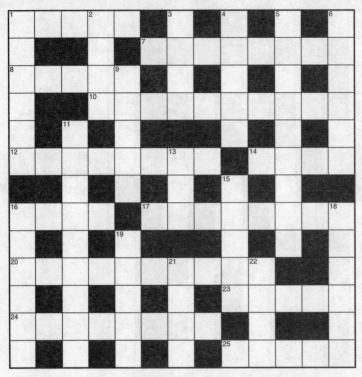

PUZZLE

145

ACROSS

1. Sailing boat
7. Convict
8. Show (to seat)
10. Jokingly
12. Status
14. Pleased
16. Hairpieces
17. Raging fires
20. Rekindled
23. Unclothed
24. Shivers
25. Tiny landmasses

DOWN

1. Adolescents
2. Part of foot
3. Boast
4. In motion
5. Nestling
6. Worn thin
9. Surprise attacks
11. Dialects
13. Persona ... grata
15. Number of days in a week
16. Heat
18. Digging tools
19. Perhaps
21. Female sheep
22. Water barriers

ACROSS

1. Hasten
4. Castle water barriers
7. Ousted
8. Fill with joy
9. Lost heat
12. Unlucky occurrence
15. One enduring pain
17. Shirked
18. Signifies
21. Keyboard player
22. Defeated person
23. Wet & windy (weather)

DOWN

1. Satisfies (thirst)
2. Coax
3. Brief letter
4. Manner
5. Grazed
6. Aromatic herb
10. Milk-processing site
11. Earthy pigment
13. Inclination
14. Matters
16. Sick feeling
18. Flour factory
19. Cowboy's boot spike
20. Fourth planet from sun

CROSSWORD

ACROSS

1. Type of cloth
5. Walk in water
7. Unnecessary
8. Food canisters
9. Diplomacy
10. The ... Wall of China
11. Pester
13. Saga
14. Mental health
18. Artist's model
21. Metal with the symbol Zn
22. Recurrent periods
24. Sixteenth of pound
25. Motion picture
26. Certain
27. Odds or ...
28. Exercise clubs
29. Comes next

DOWN

1. Receives (ball)
2. Assignments
3. Light push
4. Verb modifiers
5. Dampest
6. Decrease
12. Auction item
15. Sprightliness
16. Wages
17. More immature
19. Climbing vine
20. Staff schedules
22. Discontinue
23. Display cabinets

ACROSS

1. Fraudster
5. Word indicating action
7. Twelve months
8. Hiker's pack
9. Ambulance warnings
12. Weirdness
15. Enticed
19. Ferret relative
21. Small parrot
22. Hay bundle
23. Is mistaken
24. Reaps

DOWN

1. Most furtive
2. Hospital worker
3. Lagoons
4. Bellowed
5. Sight
6. Bread makers
10. Chamber
11. Twig shelter
12. Ancient
13. Stunned state
14. Moose
15. Overbalance
16. Foot levers
17. Entangle
18. Loses blood
19. Melted ice
20. Saunter

CROSSWORD

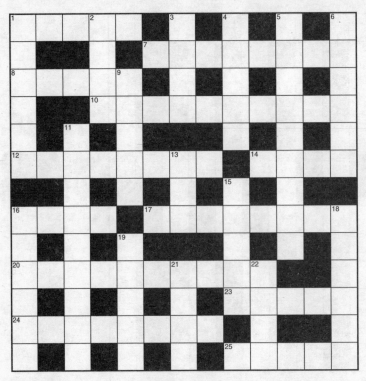

PUZZLE

149

ACROSS
1. Cogwheel set
7. Crossing out
8. Appropriately
10. Train engine
12. Snagged (stockings)
14. Became old
16. Wharf
17. Nice
20. Reproductions
23. Paintbrush hair
24. Made soapsuds
25. Agenda item

DOWN
1. Coarse sand
2. Throw (dice)
3. Office note
4. Large sweet fruit
5. Fluent in two languages
6. Consented
9. Harnesses (oxen)
11. Perfectionists
13. Conger or moray
15. Farm buildings
16. Porcupine spines
18. Illegally take
19. Merchandise
21. Mountain goat
22. Cuts (timber)

ACROSS
1. Reptiles
4. Olympic flame
7. Piglets' cries
8. Roofing stone
9. Spittle
12. Sweet-scented
15. Twelve-month old horse
17. Pardoned
18. Carpenter's tool
21. Shoe hide
22. Sly animals
23. At an incline

DOWN
1. Opulently
2. Clear (the accused)
3. Water mammal
4. Throw in air
5. Absconder
6. Rent

10. Attach (to)
11. Shuts noisily
13. Walking wearily
14. Self-contradictory statement
16. Inn
18. French singer, Edith ...
19. Spreading trees
20. Jerusalem's Wailing ...

CROSSWORD

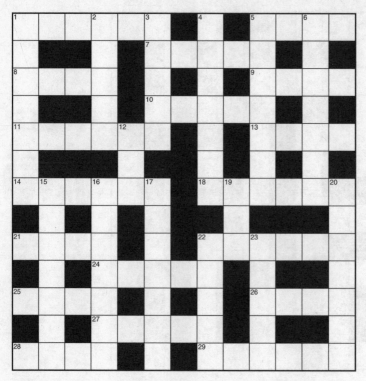

ACROSS

1. Purple shade
5. Chart-toppers
7. Care
8. Hooligan group
9. Ambition
10. Half-diameters
11. Stellar
13. Geological eras
14. Bicycle for two
18. Swarmed
21. Finger band
22. Displease
24. Moral principle
25. Wildebeests
26. Fashionable
27. Exchange
28. Tots up
29. Dutch bulb flowers

DOWN

1. Tramp
2. Light beer
3. Spin
4. Foresee
5. Dental care, oral ...
6. Cadet
12. High card
15. Straightened
16. Absorbs (food)
17. Perceive wrongly
19. Fairy
20. Draws conclusions
22. Composition for eight
23. Main (point)

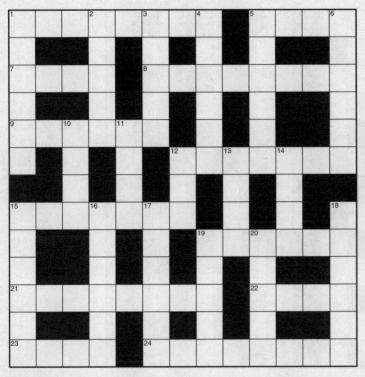

ACROSS

1. Improved
5. Dock
7. Fervent request
8. Functioned
9. Skit
12. Bothers
15. Coy
19. Muscle contractions
21. Diminish
22. Double-reed instrument
23. Mentioned
24. Made beloved

DOWN

1. Reveal
2. Modify
3. Fabric
4. Scrape (river bottom)
5. Pleasingly odd
6. Sings like Swiss mountaineer
10. Consumes
11. Musical symbol
12. Buddy
13. Leak slowly
14. Ostrich-like birds
15. Grooms' partners
16. Genetic mix
17. Hazardous
18. Go up
19. Knight's horse
20. Smell

CROSSWORD

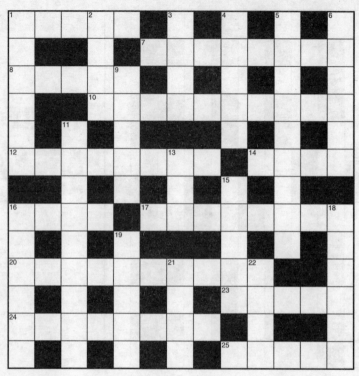

ACROSS
1. Fissure
7. Blue gem
8. Tennis ace, Rafael ...
10. Ambulance officers
12. Hatch
14. Gloomy
16. Armed fleet
17. Utterly preoccupied
20. Spectators
23. Rescued
24. Worsened (of crisis)
25. Glide on ice

DOWN
1. Are unable to
2. Applaud
3. Major Indonesian isle
4. Caught sight of
5. Inexhaustible
6. Goods thrown overboard
9. Touches down
11. Gathered (crops)
13. Ball
15. Steers off course
16. Not one person
18. Absent-minded drawing
19. Polishes (car)
21. Attracted (crowd)
22. Potato bag

CROSSWORD

ACROSS

1. Regarded smugly
4. Learn for exam
7. Edible leafstalk
8. White pointer or hammerhead
9. Wryly amusing
12. In any place
15. Conversation
17. Hung in folds
18. Flooded (of decks)
21. Citrus crop
22. Yellow part of eggs
23. Of earthquakes

DOWN

1. Chatted idly
2. Hurting
3. Dull
4. Tearful gasps
5. Unbridled
6. US city, New ...
10. Get by begging
11. Wrote on keyboard
13. Widespread disease
14. Sun umbrella
16. Brief movie guest spots
18. Wartime friend
19. Jumps on one leg
20. Louts

CROSSWORD

ACROSS
1. Unmask
5. Enclosed area
7. Rocky shelf
8. Raise
9. Rock band's sound boosters
10. Municipal chief
11. Spanish fleet
13. Subject of a verb
14. Depleted
18. Small device
21. Young horse
22. Showed assent
24. Hindu teacher
25. Festive occasion
26. Destroy
27. Molars or canines
28. Skin opening
29. Painting stands

DOWN
1. Unpacks (cargo)
2. Surplus
3. Peruvian mammal
4. Whirling (of water)
5. Desired greatly
6. Burst suddenly
12. Female hare
15. Tropical fruit
16. Throb
17. Indulged in reverie
19. In the past
20. News
22. Wall recess
23. Challenges

ACROSS

1. Cud-chewing animal
5. Domestic servant
7. Yacht canvas
8. Dormant
9. Army officers
12. Environment science
15. Qualify
19. Medium's session
21. Divide
22. Dour
23. Act
24. Speared

DOWN

1. Begin again
2. Inuit snow shelter
3. Soprano solos
4. Very sad
5. Reciprocal
6. Profoundly
10. Fair
11. Corrosion
12. Before (poetic)
13. Seep
14. Ready for business
15. Completely removed
16. Away from coast
17. Inhabitants
18. Combined forces, ... up
19. Sifting utensil
20. Quarrel

CROSSWORD

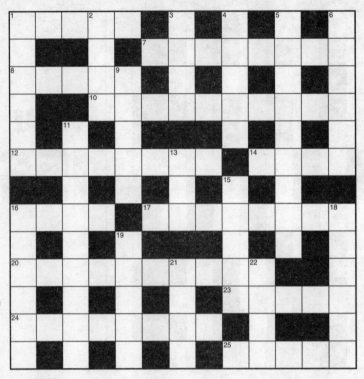

ACROSS
1. Sentence components
7. Reposition (troops)
8. Pastoral
10. Jagged wound
12. Making contact with
14. Bulk
16. Minerals
17. Ingests
20. Error
23. Alleviated
24. Fearless
25. Massage

DOWN
1. Toiler
2. Twofold
3. Hand (out)
4. Majestic
5. Swamp reptile
6. African scavengers
9. Wood-turning machine
11. Video photographer
13. At present
15. Sugar-coated
16. Hateful
18. Ranked in tennis
19. Startle
21. Metal track
22. Gape

ACROSS
1. Succumbed
4. Waist measurement
7. Perform surgery
8. Ocean giant
9. Trial
12. Grainy polishing substance
15. Drawings
17. Rasping
18. Throat part, ... cords
21. Laundry chore
22. Approaches
23. Purging

DOWN
1. Aged (of paper)
2. Pruned
3. Actress, Cameron ...
4. Expanded
5. Royal emblems
6. Flexible pipe
10. Tibetan monks
11. Rubbish
13. Coming in
14. Eye cosmetic
16. Spread (out)
18. Image-conscious
19. Reclines
20. Fly high

CROSSWORD

ACROSS

1. Of medicinal plants
5. Every single
7. Thoughts
8. Contended
9. Chowder ingredient
10. Broadcast receiver
11. Indian money units
13. Precious red gem
14. Blueprint
18. Cutting beams
21. Metal in brass
22. Reverberated
24. Stash
25. Match before final
26. Opening in fence
27. Nephew's sister
28. Male deer
29. Dress ribbons

DOWN

1. Floated in the air
2. Shift
3. Untruthful people
4. Attentive
5. Accompanies
6. Room
12. Unborn chick
15. Prominent
16. Needing a scratch
17. Invalidated
19. Rainbow shape
20. Depresses
22. Fringes
23. Peaks

ACROSS

1. Game fowl
5. Shipment
7. Wrinkle
8. Removed (badge)
9. Sewing tool
12. Postal destination
15. Jostled
19. Accommodated
21. Delivered sermon
22. Cat-o'-nine-tails

23. Complete again
24. Balances

DOWN

1. Heaping
2. Correct
3. Blue shade
4. Refilled, ... up
5. Lengthier
6. Evades
10. Listening organs
11. Sit idly

12. Emergency medicine, first ...
13. Extinct bird
14. Supplements, ... out
15. Picnic basket
16. Red salad fruit
17. Inscribes
18. Takes in (child)
19. Leafy fence
20. Unmarried

CROSSWORD

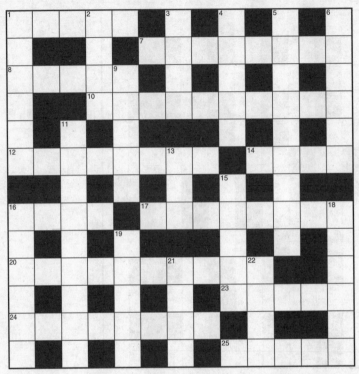

ACROSS

1. Tusk material
7. Piercing with spear
8. Onward
10. Enticement
12. Male astronaut
14. Not clearly defined
16. Sphagnum, ... moss
17. Revealed
20. Bed-cushion cover
23. Official decree
24. Highly desirable
25. African mammal, ... hippopotamus

DOWN

1. Reflections
2. Bring in (harvest)
3. Little devils
4. Suez or Panama
5. Self-appointed lawman
6. Advertising firm
9. Postpone
11. Knitted face mask
13. Give weapons to
15. Make happen
16. Ventriloquist's dummy
18. Dexterously
19. Incursion
21. Cry out
22. Swirl

ACROSS

1. Made current
4. Parish minister
7. Surprise
8. Interlace on loom
9. Procession
12. Ball-filled cushions
15. Hearing impairment
17. Taunted
18. Bad habits
21. Without weapons
22. Fine-tune
23. Error

DOWN

1. Undid (trousers)
2. Genuine
3. Small spots
4. Look at
5. Abode on wheels
6. Ready for picking
10. Flowed away
11. Ribs to hips region
13. Poorer quality
14. Waterfall
16. Cave chamber
18. Extensive
19. Be sullen
20. Ewe's young

CROSSWORD

ACROSS

1. Poked abruptly
5. Bell-shaped fruit
7. Smells foul
8. Travel permit
9. Meditation routine
10. Pale purple
11. Fatal
13. Focal points
14. Incendiary bomb material
18. Bee's liquid harvest
21. Vital part
22. Witnessing
24. Phrase
25. Pimple rash
26. Manipulative person
27. Coronet
28. Remain
29. Depends

DOWN

1. Athletics field event
2. Bold
3. Boring tool
4. Reconfigure
5. Clairvoyant
6. Branch of mathematics
12. Every
15. Peach-like fruit
16. Worry
17. Health checkup
19. Ogle
20. Respects
22. Besmirch
23. Equivalent

CROSSWORD

ACROSS

1. Armada
5. Prepare for take-off
7. Uterus
8. Shook
9. Trapped
12. Large rock
15. Instructed
19. Extreme limit
21. Muslim veils
22. Female spouse
23. Refuse to admit
24. Gained by threats

DOWN

1. Least in number
2. Underground stem
3. Very angry
4. Pure white animal
5. Journey
6. Situated inside
10. Non-alkali
11. Islamic governor
12. Auction offer
13. Module
14. James Bond film (2,2)
15. Abided by (rules)
16. Roman LXXX
17. Hire
18. Be present
19. Distraught
20. Grass-cutter

CROSSWORD

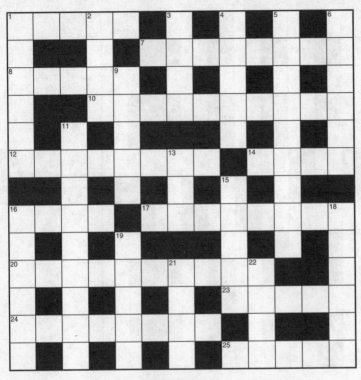

ACROSS

1. Integral
7. Unstable
8. Shrewd
10. Jingling percussion instrument
12. Meat-soaking mixture
14. Coral shipping hazard
16. Metropolis
17. Spellbinding
20. Sailor's skill
23. Lolled
24. Perceiving
25. Variety of animal

DOWN

1. Airless space
2. Parent's sister
3. Deliberately ignore
4. Black ale
5. Policy statement
6. Me
9. Spun threads
11. Prolongs
13. Arid
15. Escargot
16. Las Vegas establishment
18. Scolded
19. Knight's spear
21. Transmitted
22. Set of two

ACROSS

1. Yacht race
4. Submerged sandbank
7. Dirtying
8. Neckwear item
9. Iguana or monitor
12. Restate (position)
15. Study the heavens
17. Climbed
18. Stage

21. Not any place
22. Mountain tops
23. Walked in step

DOWN

1. Rotates
2. Lacking principles
3. Most populous continent
4. Sinks in middle
5. Narcotic drugs

6. Foliage part
10. Await with horror
11. Lawn tools
13. Offered
14. Tropical disease
16. Textile, woven ...
18. Flesh of fruit
19. Concludes
20. Move through water

CROSSWORD

ACROSS

1. The ... Of Oz
5. Traditional wisdom
7. Frostily
8. Detective's clue
9. Pen tips
10. Reasoning
11. Musical dramas
13. Weeded
14. Crockery item
18. Neglect
21. Wound crust
22. Seniors
24. Drive forward
25. In comparison to
26. Take (baby) off bottle
27. Wield (influence)
28. Narrow aperture
29. Make certain

DOWN

1. Rolls (in mud)
2. Viper
3. Clock faces
4. Moved (hips)
5. Hangs unlawfully
6. Bandits
12. Gorilla or chimpanzee
15. Liquor
16. Display case
17. Tiny waves
19. Unwell
20. Concentrated scent
22. Exclusive group
23. Ups & ...

ACROSS

1. Puffed-out (hairstyle)
5. Curved-bill wading bird
7. Vampire beasts
8. Sword holder
9. Counterbalance
12. Golfers' aides
15. Kept balls in air
19. Degraded
21. Increasing threefold
22. Fragrant flower
23. Heavy cord
24. Tirade

DOWN

1. Large monkey
2. Forgoes meals
3. Valuable possession
4. Deep shock
5. Innate
6. Four-door cars
10. Adult tadpole
11. Tea, ... Grey
12. Masticated cow food
13. Lost for words
14. Charged particles
15. Royal-court clown
16. Turkey sound
17. Improve in value
18. Hold fast (to)
19. Bad temper
20. Chef's garment

CROSSWORD

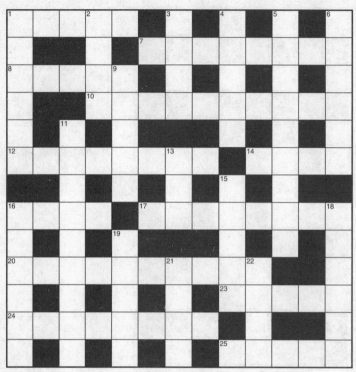

ACROSS
1. Big
7. Warm outer garment
8. Of the moon
10. Ricocheting
12. Exciting
14. Woe!
16. Witty remark
17. Of bone system
20. Overstate
23. Third planet
24. Wavered (on edge)
25. Not given food

DOWN
1. Soothed
2. Provoke
3. Elliptic
4. Batman's alter-ego, ... Wayne
5. Fashionable society person
6. Performance platforms
9. Of kidneys
11. Steered (course)
13. Rile
15. Woodwind instrument
16. Expeditions
18. Secured with rope
19. Leered at
21. Regretted
22. Gain

PUZZLE

170

ACROSS

1. Great conductor
4. Nursery story, ... tale
7. Acrobat's apparatus
8. Slow speaking style
9. Automobile repair shop
12. Cuts into four
15. Altered
17. Sitting down
18. Forgery
21. Sloping typeface
22. Reside
23. Blamed

DOWN

1. Initials motif
2. Lightning flash
3. Is indebted to
4. Nourish
5. Occupied by force
6. Shout
10. Furnish with supplies
11. Printed greetings
13. Followed closely
14. Progress
16. Scoundrel
18. Family war
19. Aromatic herb
20. Baby whale

CROSSWORD

ACROSS

1. Castigated
5. Swing to & fro
7. Kingdom
8. Brass instrument
9. Always
10. Funeral bell-ringing
11. Type of beard
13. Emblem of Wales
14. Exertion
18. Willing torturer
21. ... of Capri
22. Hauled
24. Bull-riding show
25. Feral
26. Utensil
27. Amalgamate
28. Authentic
29. Zone

DOWN

1. Tire
2. Baking agent
3. Male duck
4. Natural skills
5. Used nose
6. Eternally youthful
12. Make slip-up
15. More fastidious
16. Past arrival time
17. Vine's clinging arm
19. Dread
20. Small child
22. Sharpens
23. Ancient Mexican

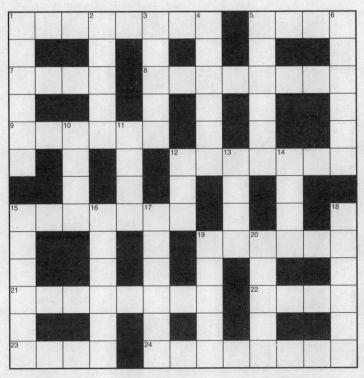

ACROSS
1. Strokes fondly
5. Delivery vehicles
7. Canned fish
8. Granting
9. Logic
12. Collected
15. Lagged behind
19. Cuts fleece off
21. Small decorative object
22. Melody
23. Conformed, ... the line
24. Impertinence

DOWN
1. Provides refreshments
2. End-of-year finals
3. Blemish
4. Skiing event
5. Visual cassettes
6. Moaned sadly
10. Spiritual glow
11. Australian gem
12. Contribute
13. Curved entrance
14. Asian sauce bean
15. Front of neck
16. Towards the middle
17. Make beloved
18. Estimate (damages)
19. Placed
20. Consumed food

CROSSWORD

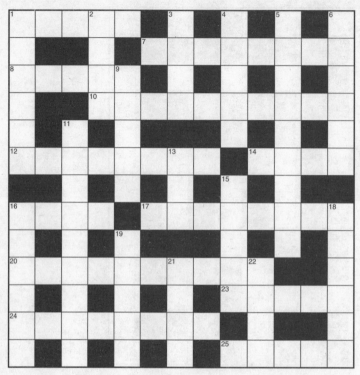

PUZZLE
173

ACROSS

1. Long exam answer
7. Most acute
8. Vindictiveness
10. Respectful attention
12. Drawing off water from
14. Those people
16. Mideast lake, ... Sea
17. Droplets of fat
20. Reset
23. Brazilian dance
24. Burnt wood
25. Smelly animal

DOWN

1. Took place after
2. Type of saxophone
3. Clarified butter
4. Orange orchard
5. In the interim
6. Small river
9. Black timber
11. Twin-hulled vessel
13. Zero
15. Woodwind instruments
16. Straight (route)
18. Harsh screech
19. Evict
21. Actor, ... Penn
22. Damp & cold

PUZZLE

174

ACROSS

1. Made duck sound
4. Speak publicly
7. Quarantine
8. Proclaim
9. Detect
12. Pertinent
15. Hand bombs
17. Australian marsupials
18. Planet's path
21. Word puzzle
22. Baby night bird
23. Army man

DOWN

1. Suppressing
2. Informal
3. Cope (with)
4. Individuals
5. Yearly book of events
6. Different
10. Grind down
11. Water bottle
13. More reliable
14. Court sport
16. Peril
18. Upon
19. Tight
20. Male sheep

	N		H		I		T		O
X	F	O	R	W	A	R	D	T	L
A		O		C	M		S	T	A	I	D
G| A	W	K	E	D		G		I	N
O|	S		R	E	A	S	O	N	E	D	D
N		C		E		S		S			I
S	T	A	R	G	A	Z	E		C		S
		R		D		S	T	A	T	I	C
C	E	D	E	S		L		M			O
H		I		W	E	A	R	I	E	D	V
A		A		A		U		R			E
R| O	C	K	Y		D	R	E	A	M	E	R

CROSSWORD

SOLUTIONS

PUZZLE 1

PUZZLE 2

PUZZLE 3

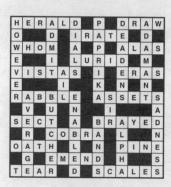

PUZZLE 4

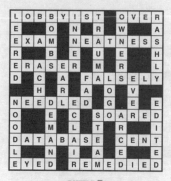

PUZZLE 5

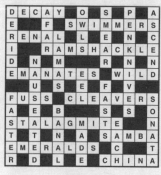

PUZZLE 6

CROSSWORD

SOLUTIONS

PUZZLE 7

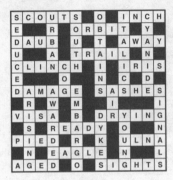

PUZZLE 8

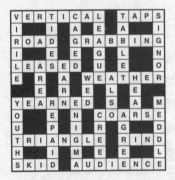

PUZZLE 9

PUZZLE 10

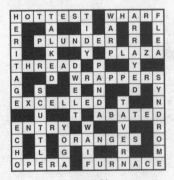

PUZZLE 11

PUZZLE 12

CROSSWORD

SOLUTIONS

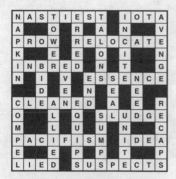

PUZZLE 13

PUZZLE 14

PUZZLE 15

PUZZLE 16

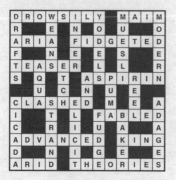

PUZZLE 17

PUZZLE 18

CROSSWORD

SOLUTIONS

PUZZLE 19

PUZZLE 20

PUZZLE 21

PUZZLE 22

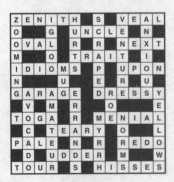

PUZZLE 23

PUZZLE 24

SOLUTIONS

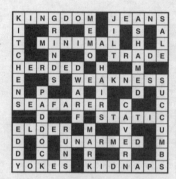

PUZZLE 25

PUZZLE 26

PUZZLE 27

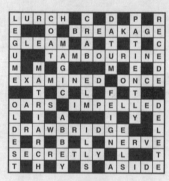

PUZZLE 28

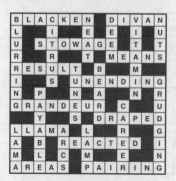

PUZZLE 29

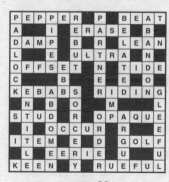

PUZZLE 30

CROSSWORD

SOLUTIONS

PUZZLE 31

PUZZLE 32

PUZZLE 33

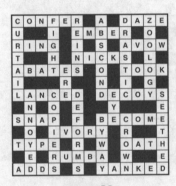

PUZZLE 34

PUZZLE 35

PUZZLE 36

CROSSWORD

SOLUTIONS

PUZZLE 37

PUZZLE 38

PUZZLE 39

PUZZLE 40

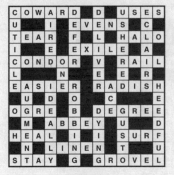

PUZZLE 41

PUZZLE 42

CROSSWORD

SOLUTIONS

PUZZLE 43

PUZZLE 44

PUZZLE 45

PUZZLE 46

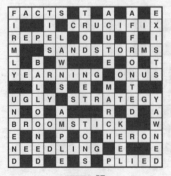

PUZZLE 47

PUZZLE 48

CROSSWORD

SOLUTIONS

PUZZLE 49

PUZZLE 50

PUZZLE 51

PUZZLE 52

PUZZLE 53

PUZZLE 54

CROSSWORD

SOLUTIONS

PUZZLE 55

PUZZLE 56

PUZZLE 57

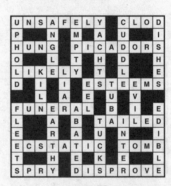

PUZZLE 58

PUZZLE 59

PUZZLE 60

SOLUTIONS

PUZZLE 61

PUZZLE 62

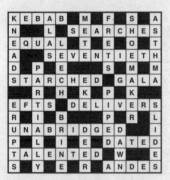

PUZZLE 63

PUZZLE 64

PUZZLE 65

PUZZLE 66

CROSSWORD

SOLUTIONS

PUZZLE 67

PUZZLE 68

PUZZLE 69

PUZZLE 70

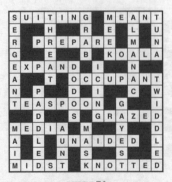

PUZZLE 71

PUZZLE 72

SOLUTIONS

PUZZLE 73

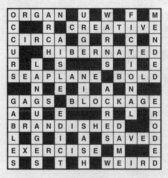

PUZZLE 74

PUZZLE 75

PUZZLE 76

PUZZLE 77

PUZZLE 78

CROSSWORD

SOLUTIONS

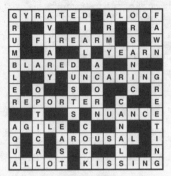

PUZZLE 79

PUZZLE 80

PUZZLE 81

PUZZLE 82

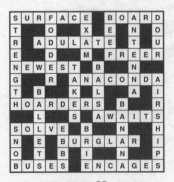

PUZZLE 83

PUZZLE 84

CROSSWORD

SOLUTIONS

PUZZLE 85

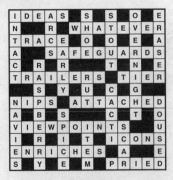

PUZZLE 86

PUZZLE 87

PUZZLE 88

PUZZLE 89

PUZZLE 90

CROSSWORD

SOLUTIONS

PUZZLE 91

PUZZLE 92

PUZZLE 93

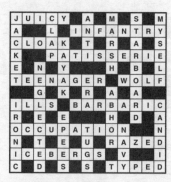

PUZZLE 94

PUZZLE 95

PUZZLE 96

CROSSWORD

SOLUTIONS

PUZZLE 97

PUZZLE 98

PUZZLE 99

PUZZLE 100

PUZZLE 101

PUZZLE 102

CROSSWORD

SOLUTIONS

PUZZLE 103

PUZZLE 104

PUZZLE 105

PUZZLE 106

PUZZLE 107

PUZZLE 108

CROSSWORD

SOLUTIONS

PUZZLE 109

PUZZLE 110

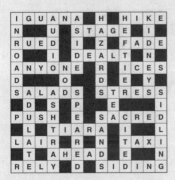

PUZZLE 111

PUZZLE 112

PUZZLE 113

PUZZLE 114

CROSSWORD

SOLUTIONS

PUZZLE 115

PUZZLE 116

PUZZLE 117

PUZZLE 118

PUZZLE 119

PUZZLE 120

CROSSWORD

SOLUTIONS

PUZZLE 121

PUZZLE 122

PUZZLE 123

PUZZLE 124

PUZZLE 125

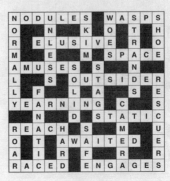

PUZZLE 126

CROSSWORD

SOLUTIONS

PUZZLE 127

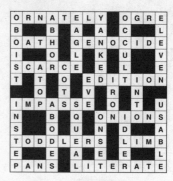

PUZZLE 128

PUZZLE 129

PUZZLE 130

PUZZLE 131

PUZZLE 132

SOLUTIONS

PUZZLE 133

PUZZLE 134

PUZZLE 135

PUZZLE 136

PUZZLE 137

PUZZLE 138

CROSSWORD

SOLUTIONS

PUZZLE 139

PUZZLE 140

PUZZLE 141

PUZZLE 142

PUZZLE 143

PUZZLE 144

CROSSWORD

SOLUTIONS

PUZZLE 145

PUZZLE 146

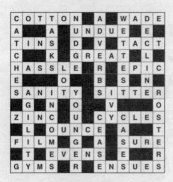

PUZZLE 147

PUZZLE 148

PUZZLE 149

PUZZLE 150

CROSSWORD

SOLUTIONS

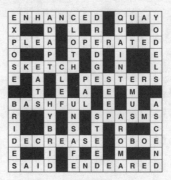

PUZZLE 151

Puzzle 151 grid:
```
V I O L E T   P   H I T S
A   A   W O R R Y   R
G A N G   I   E   G O A L
R   E   R A D I I   I
A S T R A L   I   E O N S
N   C   C   N   E
T A N D E M   T E E M E D
L   I   L   L   E
R I N G   S   O F F E N D
  G   E T H I C   O   U
G N U S   E   T   C H I C
  E   T R A D E   A   E
A D D S   R   T U L I P S
```

Puzzle 152 grid:
```
E N H A N C E D   Q U A Y
X   D   L   R   U   O
P L E A   O P E R A T E D
O   P   T   D   I   E
S K E T C H   G   N   L
E   A   L   P E S T E R S
T   E   E   A   E   M
B A S H F U L   E   U   A
R   Y   N   S P A S M S
I   B   S   T   R   C
D E C R E A S E   O B O E
E   I   F   E   M   N
S A I D   E N D E A R E D
```

PUZZLE 152

Puzzle 153 grid:
```
C R A C K   J   S   L   J
A   L   S A P P H I R E
N A D A L   V   I   M   T
N   P A R A M E D I C S
O   H   N   D   T   A
T R A P D O O R   G L U M
  R   S   R   V   E
N A V Y   O B S E S S E D
O   E   W   E   S   O
B Y S T A N D E R S   O
O   T   X   R   S A V E D
D E E P E N E D   C   L
Y   D   S   W   S K A T E
```

PUZZLE 153

Puzzle 154 grid:
```
G L O A T E D   S T U D Y
O   C   R   O   N   O
S   R H U B A R B   T   R
S   I   B   S H A R K
I R O N I C   T   M
P   G   A N Y W H E R E
E   P   D   P   D   P
D I A L O G U E   C   I
  R   E   D R A P E D
A W A S H   O   M   E
L   S   O R A N G E S   M
L   O   P   F   O   I
Y O L K S   S E I S M I C
```

PUZZLE 154

Puzzle 155 grid:
```
U N V E I L   E   Y A R D
N   X   L E D G E   U
L I F T   A   D   A M P S
O   R   M A Y O R   T
A R M A D A   I   N O U N
D   O   N   E   R
S A P P E D   G A D G E T
  V   U   R   G   I
F O A L   E   N O D D E D
  C   S W A M I   A   I
G A L A   M   C   R U I N
  D   T E E T H   E   G
P O R E   D   E A S E L S
```

PUZZLE 155

Puzzle 156 grid:
```
R U M I N A N T   M A I D
E   G   R   R   U   E
S A I L   I N A C T I V E
U   O   A   G   U   P
M A J O R S   I   A   L
E   U   U   E C O L O G Y
  S   S   R   O   P
E N T I T L E   Z   E T
R   N   O   S E A N C E
A   L   C   I   R   A
S E P A R A T E   G R I M
E   N   L   V   U   E
D E E D   S K E W E R E D
```

PUZZLE 156

CROSSWORD

SOLUTIONS

PUZZLE 157

PUZZLE 158

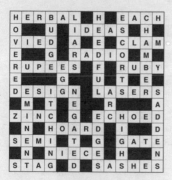

PUZZLE 159

PUZZLE 160

PUZZLE 161

PUZZLE 162

CROSSWORD

SOLUTIONS

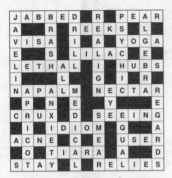

PUZZLE 163

PUZZLE 164

PUZZLE 165

PUZZLE 166

PUZZLE 167

PUZZLE 168